Mental Arithmetic 4

Answers

Schofield&Sims

TEACHER'S NOTES

Introduction

Mental arithmetic skills are fundamental to achievement in mathematics. The purpose of Schofield & Sims **Mental Arithmetic** is to provide differentiated practice tests in key areas of the maths curriculum, to be administered regularly. In addition, there is a clear focus on how number is communicated using both number vocabulary and non-verbal mathematical signs and processes.

The series consists of seven pupil books – all of them conforming to a standard layout. This ensures that pupils are not presented with too many variables at once. **Mental Arithmetic 4** contains:

- 36 one-page tests, each comprising three parts – Parts A, B and C
- two Progress Tests, with Results Charts for recording individual pupils' Progress Test results
- Check-up Tests covering number, measurement and geometry.

Parts A, B and C

Each of the 36 tests that form the bulk of the book appears on a single page and is divided into three parts (A, B and C) – the specific content of the parts is as described on the back cover. Parts A and B use pictures, symbols and simple language wherever possible so that pupils with reading difficulties will not be disadvantaged. It is suggested that one test is taken each week and that Parts A, B and C are set on separate days. Since speed with accuracy is important, a time limit of 10 minutes per part is recommended. However, you may adjust this as appropriate.

Answering the test questions

The material in each section is graded so that, before any test question is attempted, the work will usually have been covered in class. The coverage of each section is outlined on the Contents page. The term 'mental arithmetic' implies that answers only are required. For this reason, the books are presented in a one-per-pupil format, so that answers can be written in the blanks. If the pupils are allowed spare paper for workings out, remember that their responses will be slower.

Please note: You should explain to the pupils that ▓ indicates a missing number.

Marking

A separate book of answers, like this one, is available to accompany each pupil book. When the pupils have completed a test you may read out the answers as they mark their own work. If work has been done in small groups or individually, the pupils could refer to the answer book themselves.

Progress Tests

The Progress Tests, each consisting of 20 items, appear at the end of Sections 1 and 2. These are designed as timed tests, to take exactly 10 minutes each. Each Progress Test should be administered on four different occasions, under test conditions that are as similar as possible each time. So that the test can be reused, ask pupils to write their answers on a separate sheet of paper, rather than in the pupil book. Alternatively, you may photocopy a Progress Test page that has not been completed, and have the pupils write their answers on the copy. After each attempt at a Progress Test has been marked, record each pupil's results on the Results Chart provided, or invite pupils to do so themselves.

Check-up Tests

The Check-up Tests at the back of the book focus on specific topics. Administer them at the end of the school year or when a pupil finishes the book: the results will give you an insight into any areas of weakness. When the pupil moves up to a new class, the completed book should be given to the new teacher so that he or she can plan work accordingly.

CONTENTS

SECTION 1

Tests 1 to 12 (including revision of **Mental Arithmetic 3**)   **4**

Number: number and place value read, write, order and compare numbers to 1 000 000 and determine the value of each digit, count in steps of powers of 10, interpret negative numbers in context, read and write Roman numerals to 1000 (M), round any number up to 1 000 000 to the nearest 10, 100, 1000, 10 000 and 100 000; **addition and subtraction** add and subtract whole numbers with more than four digits, add and subtract numbers mentally with increasingly large numbers; **multiplication and division** identify multiples and factors of numbers, multiply numbers up to four digits by a one- or two-digit number, multiply and divide numbers mentally, divide numbers up to four digits by a one-digit number and interpret remainders appropriately, multiply and divide numbers and those involving decimals by 10, 100 and 1000, use square numbers and the notation (^{2}); **fractions (including decimals and percentages)** compare and order fractions, identify, name and write equivalent fractions of a given fraction including tenths and hundredths, add and subtract fractions with the same denominator and denominators that are multiples of the same number

Measurement: measure and calculate the perimeter of composite rectilinear shapes, calculate the area of rectangles, solve problems involving converting between units of time, use all four operations to solve problems involving measure using decimal notation including scaling

Geometry: properties of shapes estimate and compare acute, obtuse and reflex angles; **position and direction** identify, describe and represent the position of a shape following a reflection or translation

Statistics: complete, read and interpret information in tables, including timetables

Progress Test 1   **16**

SECTION 2

Tests 1 to 12 (including revision of Section 1)   **18**

Number: number and place value read, write, order and compare numbers to at least 1 000 000, recognise years written in Roman Numerals; **multiplication and division** solve problems involving addition, subtraction, multiplication and division and a combination of these, including scaling by simple fractions and problems involving simple rates; **fractions (including decimals and percentages)** read and write decimal numbers as fractions, recognise and use thousandth, round decimals with two decimal places, read, write, order and compare numbers with up to three decimal places, solve problems involving number up to three decimal places, recognise the per cent symbol (%) and understand that per cent relates to 'number of parts per hundred', recognise mixed numbers and improper fractions and convert from one form to the other

Measurement: estimate volume and capacity

Geometry: properties of shapes identify 3-D shapes from 2-D representations, identify angles at a point and one whole turn, angles on a straight line and other multiples of 90°

Statistics: solve sum and difference problems using information presented in charts and line graphs

Progress Test 2   **30**

SECTION 3

Tests 1 to 12 (including revision of Sections 1 and 2)   **32**

Number: multiplication and division use cube numbers and the notation (^{3}), solve problems involving factors and multiples, squares and cubes; **fractions (including decimals and percentages)** solve problems involving percentage, fraction and decimal equivalents

Geometry: properties of shapes use the properties of rectangles to deduce related facts and find missing lengths and angles, distinguish between regular and irregular polygons based on reasoning about equal sides and angles

Statistics: solve comparison, sum and difference problems using information presented in tables and pie charts

CHECK-UP TESTS

Number   **44**

Measurement   **46**

Measurement and geometry   **47**

A | Answer

1 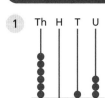 Th H T U Write in words the number shown on the abacus.

six thousand and thirteen

2 17 + 8 + 16 =   41

3 9653 − 601=   9052

4 (8 × 7) + 5 =   61

5 (56 − 8) ÷ 8 =   6

6 $\frac{7}{10}$ of 100g =   70g

7 $1\frac{3}{4}$h = ▨ min   105min

8 £1.45 = ▨ 5ps   29 5ps

9 4km 350m = ▨ m   4350m

10 850g + ▨ g = $1\frac{1}{2}$kg   650g

11 £7.09 = ▨ p   709p

12 ▨ 10ps + six 2ps = £1.82   17 10ps

B | Answer

1 Write in digits the number twelve thousand and eight.   12 008

2 How many groups of 9 are there in 6 sixes?   4

3 What is the difference in pence between £$\frac{1}{5}$ and £$\frac{1}{4}$?   5p

4 How many tens are equal to 1070?   107

5 Find the total of 53p and £1.37.   £1.90

6 By how many grams is $\frac{1}{2}$kg heavier than 280g?   220g

7 Find the cost of nine hairbands at 13p each.   £1.17

8 How many millimetres are there in 10.7cm?   107mm

9 How much change from 50p after spending 17p and 16p?   17p

10 Change to 24-hour clock times.

a 9.35 a.m.   a 09:35

b 8.50 p.m.   b 20:50

11 Find the smallest number which will divide by both 6 and 8 without a remainder.   24

12 What sum of money when multiplied by 7 equals £1.12?   16p

C | Answer

1 In a box were 48 cards. How many cards were there in seven boxes?   33̶6̶

2 *x y* In the number 7479 how many times is the 7 marked *x* greater than the 7 marked *y*?   10̶0̶

3 The temperature was 4°C and dropped by 7°C. How many degrees warmer than −5 is the new temperature?   2°C

4 The rectangular card is cut into two equal parts along a diagonal. Find the area of each part.   16cm

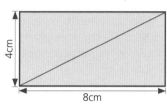
4cm / 8cm

5 What are the next two numbers in this sequence?

$\frac{1}{10}$, 1, 10, ▨ , ▨   100   100̶0̶

6 Find the difference in cost between 12 items at 3p each and 12 items at 5p each.   24̶p̶

7 A bus leaves its station at 8.40 a.m. and arrives at its destination at noon. How long does the journey take?   3h   20min

8 | Price of fabric | By how much is fabric B more expensive per metre than fabric A? |
   | A £3.96 per metre | |
   | B £4.18 per metre | |
              22̶p̶

9 The mass of cereal in a box is 425g. Find in kilograms and grams the mass of the cereal in 10 boxes.   4kg   250g

10 The minute hand of a clock turns from pointing to the number 2 to the number 8. Through how many degrees has it turned?   180°

11 A cheesecake is cut into 12 equal pieces. What fraction of the cheesecake is seven pieces? $\frac{7}{12}$

12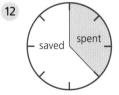
saved spent

The diagram shows how Isla used her prize money.

a What fraction did she spend?   a $\frac{3}{8}$

b The prize was £40. How much did she save?   b £25

4

A | Answer

1.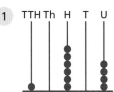

| TTH | Th | H | T | U |

Write in words the number shown on the abacus.

___ten thousand six hundred___

___and four___

2. $27 + 6 = 20 +$ ▓ — 13

3. $78 \times 6 =$ — 468

4. $872 \div 8 =$ — 109

5. £1.68 – 96p = ▓ p — 72p

6. 27 quarters = ▓ — $6\frac{3}{4}$

7. $\frac{1}{4}$ of $4.32 = — $1.08

8. 2080m = ▓ km ▓ m — 2km   80m

9. 4kg 700g = ▓ g — 4700g

10. £10 – £0.82 = — £9.18

11. 12 462 – 2300 = — 10 162

12. The time on the clock is 7min slow. Write the correct time using a.m. or p.m.

afternoon

— 5.46 p.m.

B | Answer

1. Find the missing number.
   $5000 +$ ▓ $+ 7 = 5087$ — 80

2. Write the number 145 using Roman numerals. — CXLV

3. Share £1.56 equally among six people. How much each? — 26p

4. Write 3.45m as centimetres. — 345cm

5. Which of these numbers divide by 8 without a remainder?
   12, 28, 32, 44, 56, 68 — 32, 56

6. Find the value of a $\frac{1}{5}$ of £35 — a £7
   b $\frac{4}{5}$ of £35. — b £28

7. Write 3596 to the nearest 1000. — 4000

8. How many grams in $2\frac{1}{4}$ kg? — 2250g

9. Find the change from £1 after spending 19p and 17p. — 64p

10. What is the mean average of 6cm, 9cm, 7cm and 10cm? — 8cm

11. Change to 12-hour clock times.
    a 09:05 — a   9.05 a.m.
    b 16:48 — b   4.48 p.m.

12. 10 crayons cost £1.30. Find the cost of one crayon. — 13p

C | Answer

1. A cricketer scored 12 runs short of a century. How many runs did he score? — 88

2. $37 \times 9 = 333$
   Write the value of 37×90. — 3330

3. The price of fish is £6.40 per kg. What is the cost of 1kg 500g? — £9.60

4. How many 10cm strips can be cut from a length of 5m 60cm? — 56

5. There are 20l in the petrol tank of a car. If it is $\frac{1}{3}$ full, how many more litres will it hold? — 40l

6. Find the total value of these coins. — £1.61

7. A school holiday started on 26 March and ended on 9 April. How many days' holiday were there? — 15

8. A plane is flying due east. It turns clockwise through half a right angle. Through how many degrees does it turn? — 45°

9. The diagram shows how three children shared a prize of £40. How much did each child receive?

| Josh | Sophie | Sunil |

Josh — £5
Sophie — £15
Sunil — £20

10. A train leaves at 17:50 and arrives at midnight. How long does the journey take in hours and minutes? — 6h   10min

11. The price of butter increased from £1.29 to £1.34 per 500g. How much extra is paid for 6kg? — 60p

12. 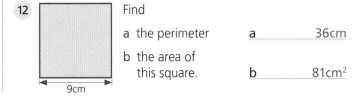 Find
    a the perimeter — a   36cm
    b the area of this square. — b   81cm²

9cm

A

		Answer
1	T U t Write in words as a decimal the number shown on the abacus.	thirty point six
2	300 + 70 + 9 tenths. Write the answer as a decimal.	370.9
3	13 624 + 5040 =	18 664
4	Round 12 467 to the nearest 10.	12 470
5	£8.70 = ▨ 10ps	87 10ps
6	20.4cm = ▨ mm	204mm
7	36.9 × 10 =	369
8	59 ÷ 10 =	5.9
9	10.7 = ▨ tenths	107 tenths
10	200g + ▨ g = 0.5kg	300g
11	2.3l = ▨ ml	2300ml
12	7, 4, 1, −2, ▨, ▨	−5 −8

B

		Answer
1	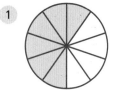 What decimal fraction of the circle is	
	a shaded	a 0.6
	b unshaded?	b 0.4
2	Write as a decimal, forty and nine tenths.	40.9
3	Of these fractions $\frac{3}{10}$, 0.5, $\frac{1}{4}$, 0.2 which is	
	a the largest	a 0.5
	b the smallest?	b 0.2
4	Find the mean average of 6, 8 and 10.	8
5	Write 300 using Roman numerals.	CCC
6	Find the cost of 100g rice at 95p per $\frac{1}{2}$kg.	19p
7	What length is 6 times longer than 4.5cm?	27cm
8	How many months in the year have 31 days?	7
9	Share £2.00 exactly among eight children. How much each?	25p
10	Write each of these quantities to the nearest whole unit.	
	a 59.8km	a 60km
	b 40.3l	b 40l
11	What number is 8 less than zero?	−8
12	How many hours and minutes from 08:50 to 11:00?	2h 10min

C

		Answer
1	 What fraction of the square is shaded?	$\frac{1}{2}$
2	Noah has 40p and Ryan has $\frac{2}{5}$ of this amount. How much have they altogether?	56p
3	On a coordinate grid point A is at (3, 4). It is then moved two squares to the right. What are its new coordinates?	(5 , 4)
4	Find in millimetres the difference between the longest and shortest of these lines.	37mm

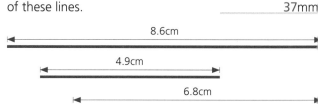

		Answer
5	Lily bought a book for £1.75 and gave seven 5ps and the rest in 10ps. How many 10ps did she give?	14 10ps
6	By how many grams is a mass of 1.4kg heavier than a mass of 850g?	550g
7	What is the date a week later than Christmas Day (25 December)?	1 January
8	Of these angles which two when added together make two right angles?	
	83° 124° 35° 107° 56°	124° 56°
9	Material for a dress costs £5.50 per metre. Find the cost of	
	a 10cm	a 55p
	b 70cm.	b £3.85
10	Two cans each hold 750ml. By how many millilitres is their total volume less than 1.8l?	300ml
11	A shopkeeper bought six pens for 95p. He sold them to make a profit of 25p. For how much did he sell each pen?	20p
12	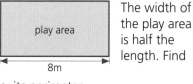 The width of the play area is half the length. Find	
	a its perimeter	a 24m
	b its area.	b 32m²

A | Answer

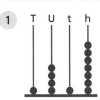

1 Write in words as a decimal the number shown on the abacus.
   <u>fourteen point one seven</u>

2 $8.03 = 8 + \dfrac{3}{\blacksquare}$ — $\dfrac{3}{100}$

3 $2.26 + 1.04 =$ — 3.3

4 £3.04 = $\blacksquare$ p — 304p

5 248cm = $\blacksquare$ m — 2.48m

6 Write $\frac{1}{4}$ as a decimal. — 0.25

7 $69\,468 - 3400 =$ — 66\,068

8 $5.07 \times 100 =$ — 507

9 Find in grams
   a 0.1 of 1kg — a 100g
   b 0.7 of 1kg. — b 700g

10 Write as a decimal 503 hundredths. — 5.03

11 Round 346\,295 to the nearest 1000. — 346\,000

12 $0.92 + \blacksquare = 1$ — 0.08

B | Answer

1 Write as a decimal, $30 + \frac{7}{10} + \frac{4}{100}$. — 30.74

2 What is the value in pence of the digit underlined?
   a £100.4<u>0</u> — a 40p
   b £15.0<u>6</u> — b 6p

3 Write in metres and centimetres 109.46m. — 109m 46cm

4 Write the missing signs +, −, × or ÷ in place of ● and ▲.
   9 ● 6 = 3 ▲ 5 — ● +   ▲ ×

5 Write as a decimal 15 tenths 7 hundredths. — 1.57

6 Decrease 0.5l by 150ml. — 350ml

7 How many hours and minutes from 2.25 p.m. to 4.05 p.m.? — 1h 40min

8 Write the missing numbers.
   a $\frac{8}{12} = \frac{\blacksquare}{3}$ — a $\frac{2}{3}$
   b $\frac{21}{24} = \frac{\blacksquare}{8}$ — b $\frac{7}{8}$

9 Divide £15 by 6 exactly. — £2.50

10 Find the area of a rectangle measuring 8.5cm by 6cm. — 51cm²

11 Divide 75kg by 100. Give the answer in grams. — 750g

12 Which of these fractions are of equal value?
   $\frac{3}{4}$ 0.6 0.75 $\frac{7}{10}$ — $\frac{3}{4}$, 0.75

C | Answer

1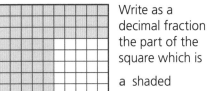
   Write as a decimal fraction the part of the square which is
   a shaded — a 0.65
   b unshaded. — b 0.35

2 Badges cost 6p each. How many can be bought for £1.56? — 26

3 A teaspoon holds 5ml. How many spoonfuls in $\frac{1}{4}$l? — 50

4 Find the missing number in this division.
   $9\,\overline{)\,\blacksquare\,\blacksquare\,\blacksquare}$ quotient 1 7 r 7 — 160

5 Mince costs €1.80 per $\frac{1}{2}$kg. Find the cost of mince weighing 600g. — €2.16

6 A triangle has two equal sides each measuring 36cm. Its perimeter is 1m. Find the length of the third side. — 28cm

7 There were 6845 people at a concert. Write this number
   a to the nearest 100 — a 6800
   b to the nearest 10. — b 6850

8 There are two 2 place decimal numbers which are greater than 3.97 but less than 4.00. What are the numbers? — 3.98 3.99

9 Fatima collected 150 pennies for the school fund. Olivia collected 3 times as many. How many £1 coins did they receive in exchange? — 6

10 Jamie's stride measures 40cm. How many strides will he take in walking 10m? — 25

11 A rectangular path measures 9m long and 50cm wide. Find its area in m². — 4.5m²

12 cm
   A |———|———|———|———|———|———|———|———| B

   The line AB is drawn to a scale 1cm to 20cm. Find the length the line represents
   a in centimetres — a 160cm
   b in millimetres. — b 1600mm

A | Answer

1. Write as a decimal $10 + \frac{3}{10} + \frac{7}{100}$ — 10.37
2. $(8 \times 9) + (0 \times 7) =$ — 72
3. $10.05m = \square$ cm — 1005cm
4. $250g + \square g = 600g$ — 350g
5. $0.5l = 330ml + \square$ ml — 170ml
6. $\frac{3}{8}$ of £40 = — £15
7. $296\,483 - 20\,210 =$ — 276 273
8. £2.08 – 70p = £ $\square$ — £1.38
9. Write $\frac{3}{5}$ as a decimal fraction. — 0.6
10. 3h 40min = $\square$ min — 220min
11. $40.08 \times 100 =$ — 4008
12. £8.32 ÷ 4 = — £2.08

B | Answer

1.

   Write as a decimal fraction the part of the strip which is
   a shaded — a 0.3
   b unshaded. — b 0.7
2. What number is 7 more than 6 × 8? — 55
3. a Name the eleventh month of the year. — a November
   b How many days are there in that month? — b 30
4. Find the cost of 100g at £1.40 per kilogram. — 14p
5. Find the difference between the largest and smallest of these fractions.
   $\frac{3}{10}, \frac{1}{2}, \frac{4}{5}, \frac{7}{10}$ — $\frac{5}{10}$ or $\frac{1}{2}$
6. Write 19l 720ml to the nearest litre. — 20l
7. Which number is 5 less than –2? — –7
8. Find the area in m² of a floor measuring 8m by 3m 50cm. — 28m²
9. Complete this number sequence.
   0.3, 3, 30, $\blacksquare$, $\blacksquare$ — 300   3000
10. Divide 30.4cm into 8 equal parts. Find the length of each part. — 3.8cm
11. How many 20ps must be added to three 10ps to equal £2.10? — 9 20ps
12.

    Of these triangles which is
    a isosceles — a B
    b equilateral? — b C

C | Answer

1. One thousand and six people each bought five tickets. How many tickets was that altogether? — 503C
2. How much change from three 20ps after paying for six eggs at £1.08 per dozen? — 6p
3.

   Write the length of each line in centimetres.
   AB — 4.7cm
   CD — 6.2cm
4. Find the mean average mass of 14kg, 10kg and 9kg. — 11kg
5. Dasal spent $\frac{1}{4}$ of his money on sweets and $\frac{3}{8}$ on bus fares. What fraction of his money is left? — $\frac{3}{8}$
6. How many degrees are there in each of the equal angles at the centre of the circle? — 60°
7. How many grams less than 1kg is the total mass? — 350g
8. Tom's date of birth is 7 March 1995. Daniel was born exactly 4 years later. Write Daniel's date of birth in digits. — 7.3.1999
9. The approximate distance between two villages is given as 11km. The actual distance is 10.7km. Find the difference in metres. — 300m
10. Which two of these fractions are equivalent to $\frac{3}{4}$?
    $\frac{6}{10}, \frac{9}{12}, \frac{4}{5}, \frac{15}{20}$ — $\frac{9}{12}$ $\frac{15}{20}$
11. Emily and Katie have 60p between them. Emily has 8p more than Katie. How much has each?
    a Emily — a 34p
    b Katie — b 26p
12. Find the missing measurement marked b. — 30m
    area 3000m²   100m

8

A | Answer

1. 45p + 35p + £1.20 = £☐ ····· £2.00

2. 63 ÷ 8 = ····· 7 r 7

3. Write as a decimal 708 hundredths. ····· 7.08

4. $\frac{1}{2}$kg − ☐ g = 125g ····· 375g

5. £1.05 × 6 = ····· £6.30

6. 0.8 + ☐ = 1 ····· 0.2

7. How many minutes from 9.27 a.m. to 11.15 a.m.? ····· 108min

8. ☐ ml + 4050ml = 5l ····· 950ml

9. 60.4 ÷ 10 = ····· 6.04

10. $\frac{3}{5} = \frac{☐}{100}$ ····· $\frac{60}{100}$

11. 0.5 of $17.20 = ····· $8.60

12. 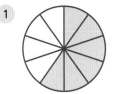 ∠ A + ∠ B + ∠ C = ☐° ····· 180°

B | Answer

1. 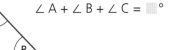 Write the part which is shaded

   a as a simple fraction ····· a $\frac{3}{5}$

   b as a decimal fraction. ····· b 0.6

2. From 9 times 7 take 5. ····· 58

3. Write the 24-hour clock time for 12min before midnight. ····· 23:48

4. Find the cost of 20cm at 75p per metre. ····· 15p

5. Write 9kg 870g to the nearest $\frac{1}{2}$kg. ····· 10kg

6. Find the difference between 3.8l and 6l. ····· 2.2l

7. What length in centimetre is $\frac{1}{5}$ of 3m? ····· 60cm

8. Find the total of $2\frac{1}{4}$, $3\frac{5}{8}$ and 5. ····· $10\frac{7}{8}$

9. How many 2ps are worth £2.48? ····· 124 2ps

10. A square has sides measuring 10cm.

    Find a its perimeter ····· a 40cm

    b its area. ····· b 100cm²

11. Complete the number sequence.

    0.01, 0.1, 1, ☐, ☐ ····· 10 100

12. Which of these triangles is

    a a right-angled triangle ····· a B

    b an acute-angled triangle ····· b C

    c an obtuse-angled triangle? ····· c A

C | Answer

1. Find the total of $\frac{3}{4}$kg, 400g and 200g. Write the answer in kilograms and grams. ····· 1kg 350g

2. What is the value of the digit underlined in each of these numbers?

   a 60<u>3</u>7 ····· a 30

   b 49.0<u>8</u> ····· b 8 hundredths

3. Find the mean average number of dots in a row. ····· 5

4. Samina bought eight sweets at 4p each. How much change had she from 50p? ····· 18p

5. How many degrees are there in the angle marked A? ····· 115°

6. The population of a town is 18 968. Write the number

   a to the nearest 1000 ····· a 19 000

   b to the nearest 100. ····· b 19 000

7. Find the smallest number which can be added to 40 to make a number which is exactly divisible by 7. ····· 2

8. Five balloons cost 45p. Find the cost of three balloons. ····· 27p

9. Six children each had an equal share of a sum of money. They each received 18p and there was 2p left over. Find the sum of money. ····· £1.10

10. Two angles of a triangle each measure 45°. Find the size in degrees of the third angle. ····· 90°

11. What liquid measure is equal to 0.1 of 20l? ····· 2l

12.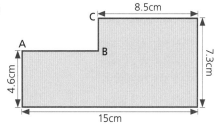

    Find the length of

    a the side AB ····· a 6.5cm

    b the side BC. ····· b 2.7cm

A | Answer

1. $\frac{7}{12} + \blacksquare = 1$ — $\frac{5}{12}$
2. Write as a decimal $15 + \frac{5}{100}$ — 15.05
3. $20.4 = \blacksquare$ tenths — 204 tenths
4. $(8 \times 8) + 6 =$ — 70
5. $2km + \frac{1}{2}km + \frac{1}{4}km = \blacksquare m$ — 2750m
6. Find the missing number.
   $3000 + 100 + \blacksquare + 6 = 3196$ — 90
7. £2.00 − 46p = £$\blacksquare$ — £1.54
8. $700g + \blacksquare g = 1.5kg$ — 800g
9. How many thirds in $6\frac{2}{3}$? — $\frac{20}{3}$
10. The time on the clock is 13min fast. Write the correct time using a.m. or p.m. — 6.54 p.m.

    evening
11. 27p × 4 = — £1.08
12. $0.7l - \blacksquare ml = 610ml$ — 90ml

B | Answer

1. $5^2 = 5 \times 5 = 25$.
   Find the value of   a 6^2 — a 36
   b 10^2. — b 100
2. Add 8 hundredths to 3.04. — 3.12
3. What is the difference between 90p and £3.25? — £2.35
4. How many hours and minutes are there in 105 min? — 1h 45min
5. Find the cost of seven lemons at 18p each. — £1.26
6. Fill in the missing numbers.
   a $\frac{8}{20} = \frac{2}{\blacksquare}$ — a $\frac{2}{5}$
   b $\frac{25}{100} = \frac{1}{\blacksquare}$ — b $\frac{1}{4}$
7. How many grams must be added to 2300g to make $2\frac{1}{2}$ kg? — 200g
8. Write 600 using Roman numerals. — DC
9. How many degrees are there in the angle marked A? — 120°
10. By how many millimetres is 8.3cm longer than 56mm? — 27mm
11. Divide £3.68 into 8 equal parts. What is the value in pence of each part? — 46p
12. $(8 \times 6) = (3 \times 6) + (x \times 6)$
    Find the number x stands for. — 5

C | Answer

1. Write in digits the number which is 70 less than ten thousand. — 9930
2. Count the value of these coins in the given order and find the total amount. — £1.72

   10 10p   50 50p   5 5p   20 20p   2p
3. All the angles at the centre of the circle are equal. How many degrees are there in the marked angle? — 45°
4. 1l of water has a mass of 1kg. Find in grams the mass of water in a bottle which holds $\frac{1}{4}$ l. — 250g
5. Give the size in degrees of
   a angle A — a 45°
   b angle B. — b 90°
6. In a test, James scored 70 out of 100. What fraction (with the denominator 10) of the total did he score? — $\frac{7}{10}$
7. Chloe has £1.50 and Anna has $\frac{3}{5}$ of this amount. How much have they altogether? — £2.40
8. How many days are there from 28 June to 9 July? Do not count the first day. — 11
9. Find the mean average of 5, 6, 7, 8 and 9. — 7
10. The driveway is 3 times as long as it is wide.
    Find   a its length — a 60m
    b its perimeter. — b 160m

    driveway   20m
11. By how many m² is the area of the driveway more than 1000m²? — 200m²
12. Leo doubles his savings every week for 4 weeks. In the first week he saved 20p. How much did he save in the fourth week? — £1.60

A | Answer

1. $6.07 = \blacksquare$ hundredths — **607** hundredths

2. Write as a 24-hour clock time 16 minutes after midnight. — **00:16**

3. Write as a decimal $200 + \frac{3}{10} + \frac{9}{100}$ — **200.39**

4. $485\,472 + 10\,303 =$ — **495\,775**

5. Find the value of x if $54 \div 9 = 30 \div x$ — **5**

6. £1.00 − (four 10ps + nine 5ps) = $\blacksquare$ p — **15p**

7. $40° + 65° + \blacksquare° = 180°$ — **75°**

8. $\frac{1000}{8} =$ — **125**

9. £4.86 = $\blacksquare$ 10ps + 6p — **48** 10ps

10. $\blacksquare$ ml × 10 = 2l — **200ml**

11. £2.34 ÷ 6 = $\blacksquare$ p — **39p**

12. 425g + 70g + 87g = $\blacksquare$ kg — **0.582kg**

B | Answer

1. Add 5 to 7^2. — **54**

2. Change these times to 12-hour clock times using a.m. or p.m.

   a 07:05 — a **7.05 a.m.**

   b 23:20 — b **11.20 p.m.**

3. Decrease £1.34 by 40p. — **94p**

4. Write to the nearest whole number.

   a $9\frac{7}{10}$ — a **10**

   b $20\frac{2}{5}$ — b **20**

5. By how many metres is 1850m less than 3km? — **1150m**

6. Find the total of fifteen 20ps and twelve 10ps. — **£4.20**

7. What is the difference in millilitres between $\frac{3}{4}$l and 580ml? — **170ml**

8. How many grams are equal to 0.3kg? — **300g**

9. How many degrees are there in each of the equal angles at the centre of the circle? — **45°**

10. $\frac{1}{2}$kg costs £1.60. Find the cost of 100g. — **32p**

11. Find the area of a square with sides of 40cm. — **1600cm²**

12. $612 \div y = 6$. Find y. — **102**

C | Answer

1. By how many is 10^2 greater than 9^2? — **19**

2. How many

   a tenths are equal to 50.6 — a **506** tenths

   b hundredths are equal to 40.75? — b **4075** hundredths

3. 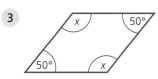 The four angles of any quadrilateral together equal 360°. Find in degrees the size of the angles marked x. — **130°**

4. Seven nails have a mass of 50g. How many nails have a mass of $\frac{1}{2}$kg? — **70**

5. Through how many degrees does the hour hand of a clock turn from noon to 4.00 p.m.? — **120°**

6. Write these numbers so that the value of the digit 7 in each number is 7 hundredths.

   a 1607 — a **16.07**

   b 97 — b **0.97**

7. A right-angled triangle contains an angle of 55°. Find the size of the third angle. — **35°**

8. When a barrel is $\frac{1}{5}$ full it holds 16l. How many litres will it hold when $\frac{1}{2}$ full? — **40l**

9. Find to the nearest kilometre the distance by road from Batey to Skipley. — **20km**

10. A game which costs £17.50 is paid for at the rate of 50p per week. How many payments are made? — **35**

11. A bus runs at 20min intervals. If the first bus leaves at 07:30, find the starting time of the third bus. — **08:10**

12. What is the cost of 1kg 200g at 35p per kilogram? — **42p**

SECTION 1 | Test 9

A

		Answer
1	375 375 + 420 001 =	795 376
2	200 − 97 =	103
3	$\frac{3}{10}$ of 50p =	15p
4	Write as a decimal 70 + 6 + $\frac{9}{100}$	76.09
5	2km 350m = ▉m	2350m
6	£1.71 ÷ 9 = ▉p	19p
7	1.5kg − 650g = ▉g	850g
8	Write 750 using Roman numerals.	DCCL
9	1150ml + ▉ml = 2l	850ml
10	215min = ▉h ▉min	3h 35min
11	£3.05 = ▉ 10ps + one 5p	30 10ps
12	4.5kg × 100 =	450kg

B

		Answer
1	What is the value of the missing number? Thirty point three six = 30 + ▉ + $\frac{6}{100}$	$\frac{3}{10}$
2	Write to the nearest metre 19.54m.	20m
3	Find the change from £5.00 after spending 89p.	£4.11
4	What number is 5 more than −4?	1
5	Change 8.35 p.m. to 24-hour clock time.	20:35
6	An isosceles triangle has two angles of 70°. What is the size of the third angle?	40°
7	Find in millimetres the length of a line that is half of 7.6cm.	38mm
8	Increase €1.20 by a quarter of €1.20.	€1.50
9	Name the pair of parallel lines in this shape.	AB and CD
10	How many times can 250ml be taken from $2\frac{1}{2}$l?	10
11	Find the cost of 1kg 100g of oranges at 50p per $\frac{1}{2}$kg.	£1.10
12	Which of these decimal fractions is equal to $\frac{3}{4}$? 0.34, 0.43, 0.75, 0.63	0.75

C

		Answer
1	Arrange the digits 3, 8, 0, 5 to make	
	a the largest possible number	a 8530
	b the smallest possible number.	b 0358
2	This shape has eight equal sides.	
	a Name the shape.	a octagon
	b How many degrees are there in ∠ A?	b 45°
3	Share £4.76 equally among seven children. Find how much each has. Write the answer	
	a in pence	a 68p
	b in £s.	b £0.68
4	A teaspoon holds 5ml. What decimal fraction of a litre is contained in 100 spoonfuls?	0.5l
5	Find in grams. a 0.1 kg	a 100g
	b 0.4 kg	b 400g
	c 0.8 kg	c 800g
6	The perimeter of the rectangle is 96cm. The width is 15cm. Find its length.	33cm
7	What is the largest of these decimal numbers? 1.1, 0.98, 1.12, 1.06	1.12
8	The thickness of 100 sheets of card is 14.5cm. Find the thickness in millimetres of	
	a 10 sheets	a 14.5mm
	b one sheet.	b 1.45mm
9	These angles are equal. a How many right angles are equal to the sum of the five angles?	a 4
	b How many degrees are there in each of the five angles?	b 72°
10	Tissues are sold at five for 35p. What is paid for 30 tissues?	£2.10
11	Alfie spent $\frac{3}{5}$ of his money on sweets and $\frac{3}{10}$ on ice cream. What fraction of his money had he left?	$\frac{1}{10}$
12	Marek 10 years, Harry 9 years, Evie ▉ years, Becky 10 years. The mean average age of the children is 9 years. How old is Evie?	7yr

A | Answer

1. Write as a decimal
   a 407 tenths — **a 40.7**
   b 209 hundredths. — **b 2.09**

2. How many days in 1 year? — **365**

3. $4^2 + 3^2 - 2^2 =$ — **21**

4. 50p + two 20ps = ▨ 5ps — **18 5ps**

5. 0.55 + ▨ = 1 — **0.45**

6. $\frac{9}{10}$ of 1kg = ▨ g — **900g**

7. 63 ÷ 7 = 54 ÷ ▨ — **6**

8. $\frac{2}{5} + \frac{5}{10} =$ — **$\frac{9}{10}$**

9. 0.48m ÷ 8 = ▨ cm — **6cm**

10. £2.30 − 95p = £▨ — **£1.35**

11. 87 × 6 = — **522**

12. Write as a decimal,
    9 + 3 tenths + 17 hundredths. — **9.47**

B | Answer

1. Write the value of the digit underlined.
   a 36.0<u>9</u> — **a 9 hundredths**
   b 1<u>8</u>0.6 — **b 80**

2. By how many grams is 1.3kg heavier than 700g? — **600g**

3. Find the cost of eight tomatoes at 19p each. — **£1.52**

4. By what length is 0.5m less than 10.05m? — **9.55m**

5. Write the 24-hour clock time which is 17min later than 13:55. — **14:12**

6. How many 12p eggs can be bought for £1.80? — **15**

7. Which two of these fractions when added together make a whole one?
   $\frac{5}{8}, \frac{2}{5}, \frac{1}{4}, \frac{6}{10}, \frac{1}{8}$ — **$\frac{2}{5}$ $\frac{6}{10}$**

8. Find the average of 1.6l, 0.8l, 1.2l. — **1.2l**

9. Write 284 using Roman numerals. — **CCLXXXIV**

10. Find in centimetres the length of a line that is twice 85mm. — **17cm**

11. Round 295 373 to the nearest 1000. — **295 000**

12. Find the perimeter of a rectangle 12.5cm long and 3.5cm wide. — **32cm**

C | Answer

1. What is the greatest possible remainder when a whole number is divided by 9? — **8**

2. How many pieces of ribbon each 4.5cm long can be cut from a length of $4\frac{1}{2}$m? — **100**

3. A bag of rice having a mass of 200g costs 40p. Find the price per kilogram. — **£2.00**

4. What is the 12-hour clock time which is $1\frac{1}{4}$h earlier than 13:05? Use a.m. or p.m. — **11.50 a.m.**

5. Eggs are packed in boxes in layers of 20. If there are four layers in each box and five boxes, find the total number of eggs. — **400**

6.
```
     £
   8.6 0    What is the missing
   ▨.▨▨     sum of money?        £5.50
 + 2.9 0
  1 7.0 0
```

7. How many degrees are there in the angle marked y? — **60°**

8. 15 × 36 = 540. By how many is 16 × 36 more than 540? — **36**

9. A 2l can is $\frac{7}{10}$ full. How many more millilitres are required to fill it? — **600ml**

10. A map is drawn to a scale 1cm to 10km. Find the actual distance represented by 54mm. — **54km**

11. How many right angles are equal to the sum of the three angles in a triangle? — **2**

12. How many tiles each 10cm square are needed to cover the area shown? — **24**

A | Answer

1. $(7 \times 8) + 5 =$ _____ 61
2. $2.86 =$ ▦ tenths + 6 hundredths _____ 28 tenths
3. $\frac{4}{5} = \frac{▦}{100}$ _____ $\frac{80}{100}$
4. $£2.04 \times 8 =$ _____ £16.32
5. How many minutes from 11.40 a.m. to 1.10 p.m.? _____ 90min
6. $105\,570 - 100\,510 =$ _____ 5060
7. $4kg\ 50g =$ ▦ g _____ 4050g
8. $70p \times 2\frac{1}{2} =$ _____ £1.75
9. $504mm =$ ▦ cm _____ 50.4cm
10. $\angle A + \angle B + \angle C + \angle D =$ ▦ ° _____ 360°
11. $0.3l =$ ▦ ml _____ 300ml
12. $£9.00 \div 100 =$ ▦ p _____ 9p

B | Answer

1. Take 0 times 9 from the product of 8 and 6. _____ 48
2. Five parcels of different sizes have a total mass of 800g. Find their average mass. _____ 160g
3. Decrease 72p by $\frac{1}{8}$. _____ 63p
4. In a leap year February has 29 days. How many days in a leap year? _____ 366
5. Write 9l 700ml to the nearest half-litre. _____ $9\frac{1}{2}l$
6. How much change from a £5 note after first spending £3 and then 56p? £1.44
7. Which of these fractions equal $\frac{2}{3}$? $\frac{4}{9}, \frac{8}{12}, \frac{16}{20}, \frac{10}{15}$ _____ $\frac{8}{12}$ $\frac{10}{15}$
8. What number when multiplied by 3 gives 207 for the answer? _____ 69
9. Find the cost of 2m 20cm at 25p per metre. _____ 55p
10. Write 493 using Roman numerals. _____ CDXCIII
11. $17 \times 7 = 119$. Write the answer to 0.17×7. _____ 1.19
12. Which of these lines are perpendicular to the line XY? _____ b, e

C | Answer

1. Write the next two odd numbers in this sequence. 995, 997, 999, ▦, ▦ _____ 1001 _____ 1003
2. Pasta costs 25p for 100g. Find the cost of a bag of pasta containing 1kg 300g. _____ £3.25
3. Write each of these fractions with a denominator of 100.
   a $\frac{9}{10}$ — a $\frac{90}{100}$
   b $\frac{7}{10}$ — b $\frac{70}{100}$
   c $\frac{13}{50}$ — c $\frac{26}{100}$
4. The rainfall for three months of a year was 37mm, 43mm, 40mm. Find the average monthly rainfall. _____ 40mm
5. Find   a the area of the rectangle — a _____ 20cm²
         b the perimeter of the rectangle. — b _____ 24cm

Write the unit of measurement in each case.

6. The temperature was 4°C and it fell by 9°C. What is the temperature now? _____ −5°C
7. In this right-angled triangle what is the size in degrees of $\angle A$? _____ 50°
8. Find the mean average of these numbers.

| 7 | 13 | 6 | 9 | 5 |

_____ 8

9. Jack needs £3.20 to buy a book. He has saved three 50ps, four 20ps and one 10p. How much more must he save? _____ 80p
10. A train journey from London to Leeds takes 2h 35min. At what time do these trains arrive at Leeds if they leave London at
    a 11:25 — a 14:00
    b 18:45? — b 21:20
11. 1 litre of water has a mass of 1kg. Find the mass of a bottle containing 1.5l of water if the bottle has a mass of 150g. _____ 1kg _____ 650g
12. On a coordinate grid, point A is at (5, 2). It is then moved three squares up. What are its coordinates now? _____ (5 , 5)

A

		Answer
1	300 + 15 + 5000 =	5315
2	forty-five 5ps = £ ▧	£2.25
3	$\frac{27}{100}$ of 1m = ▧ cm	27cm
4	0.45 + ▧ = 1	0.55
5	The ninth month of the year is ▧.	September
6	709 × 8 =	5672
7	3.7 = ▧ hundredths	370 hundredths
8	17p + 15p + 20p = £ ▧	£0.52
9	140g + ▧ g = 0.2kg	60g
10	£23.00 ÷ 5 =	£4.60
11	$0.7l - \frac{1}{2}l$ = ▧ ml	200ml
12	$\frac{3}{10} + \frac{2}{5}$ =	$\frac{7}{10}$

B

		Answer
1	What number is 32 greater than 290?	322
2	Write as a decimal 5 tens plus 18 tenths.	51.8
3	How many 5ps must be taken from three 50ps to leave £1.15?	7 5ps
4	How many eighths are there in $7\frac{5}{8}$?	$\frac{61}{8}$
5	29 June is on a Friday. On which day is 4 July?	Wednesday
6	Share 75p equally among eight children. Find	
	a how much they each receive	a 9p
	b how much is left over.	b 3p
7	What mass in kilograms is double 3kg 750g?	7.5kg
8	Which of these numbers will divide exactly by both 6 and 9 without a remainder? 24 36 48 63	36
9	Find the area of a rectangular playground 30m long and 18m wide.	540m²
10	Find the cost of 400g at 25p per kilogram.	10p
11	From $1\frac{3}{8}$ subtract $(\frac{1}{2} + \frac{3}{4})$.	$\frac{1}{8}$
12	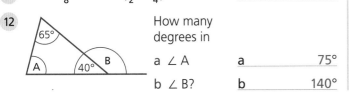 How many degrees in a ∠ A	a 75°
	b ∠ B?	b 140°

C

		Answer
1	Approximate	
	a 9.82 to the nearest whole one	a 10
	b £10.48 to the nearest £1	b £10
	c 3.25kg to the nearest kilogram.	c 3kg
2	The kilometre reading on a car is 9946.2. What distance has the car to travel for it to read ten thousand kilometres?	53.8km
3	Which two shapes are reflections of each other along the dotted line?	H E

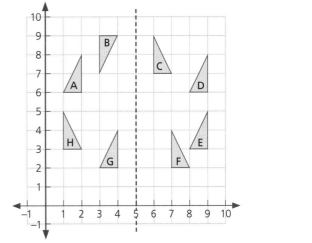

		Answer
4	10 yoghurts cost £2.40. Find the cost of three.	72p
5	Josh was born on 30/06/03. Write his age in years and months on 1 September 2015.	12yr 2mth
6	Find the sum of the numbers between 60 and 80 which are divisible by 9.	135
7	Write the number 900 using Roman numerals.	CM
8	1000 teabags have a mass of 4.2kg. Find the mass in grams of	
	a 100 teabags	a 420g
	b one teabag.	b 4.2g
9	A shopkeeper bought six balls for £1.32 and sold them to make a total profit of 48p. For how much did he sell each ball?	30p
10	A car uses 7l of petrol to travel 100km. How many litres are required for 1600km?	112l
11	Three lines measure 0.04m, 47mm, 3.8cm. Find the difference between the longest and shortest lines.	9mm
12	Find the mean average of these prices. 26p 10p 25p 32p 17p	22p

Write the numbers 1 to 20 down the side of a piece of paper.
Write alongside these numbers the **answers only** to the following questions.
Work as quickly as you can. Time allowed – **10 minutes**.

1 Write in digits to the nearest hundred
six thousand four hundred and fifty.
_____ 6500

2 Find the missing number of 5ps.
£1.65 = two 50ps, two 20ps, ▓ 5ps
_____ 5 5ps

3 Round 463 596 to the nearest 10.
_____ 463 600

4 Write as a decimal the sum of 3 hundreds and 109 hundredths.
_____ 301.09

5 How many hours and minutes from 11.52 a.m. to 2.27 p.m.?
_____ 2h 35min

6 By counting in the given order find the total value of the coins.
_____ 95p

7 Write the number 731 using Roman numerals.
_____ DCCXXXI

8 On a coordinate grid, point A is at (5, 4). It is then moved four squares to the left.
What are its coordinates now?
_____ (1, 4)

9 $\frac{3}{4}$ of a sum of money is 54p. Find the whole amount.
_____ 72p

10 26 × 8 = 208. Write the answer to 26 × 80.
_____ 2080

11 Find the mean average of these prices.
| 31p | 50p | 40p | 44p | 30p |
_____ 39p

12 Take 650ml from 5l and give the answer to the nearest 0.5l.
_____ 4.5l

13 A regular hexagon has sides each measuring 58mm. Find its perimeter in centimetres.
_____ 34.8cm

14 200g of mushrooms cost 48p. Find the price of the mushrooms per half-kilogram.
_____ £1.20

15 How many less than 870 000 is the answer to 859 985 + 10 014?
_____ 1

16 A rectangular garden plot measures 12.8m long and 8m wide. Find its area in m².
_____ 102.4m²

17

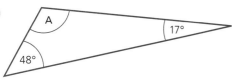 Find the size of angle A.
_____ 115°

18 The mass of a 10p coin is 6.5g. Find the mass in kilograms of the coins in a £10 bag of 10ps.
_____ 0.65kg

19 What is the 12-hour clock time which is $2\frac{1}{4}$h earlier than 14:25? Use a.m. or p.m.
_____ 12.10 p.m.

20 0.97 + ▓ = 1
_____ 0.03

You will work through Progress Test 1 at **four** different times – once at the end of Section 1, then again after you have completed each of Section 2 Test 4, Test 8 and Test 11.

When you first complete the test:

a colour the first column to show the number of answers correct out of 20

b enter the date.

Each time you take the test, enter the result and the date in the marked columns.

	1st	2nd	3rd	4th
20				
19				
18				
17				
16				
15				
14				
13				
12				
11				
10				
9				
8				
7				
6				
5				
4				
3				
2				
1				
0				
date				

number of answers correct

A | Answer

1. Write in digits thirty thousand and fifteen. — 30 015
2. $2006 - 600 =$ — 1406
3. three 10ps and six 5ps = ▨ 2ps — 30 2ps
4. $10.04 =$ ▨ hundredths — 1004 hundredths
5. $56 \times 20 =$ — 1120
6. 36cm = ▨m — 0.36m
7. 0.850kg = ▨g — 850g
8. $0.05 + 0.04 =$ — 0.09
9. $0.5 \times 3 =$ — 1.5
10. $29 + 13 = 7 \times$ ▨ — 6
11. £0.95 = three 20ps + ▨ 5ps — 7 5ps
12. $\frac{9}{100}$ of £3.00 = ▨p — 27p

B | Answer

1. Write 639 using Roman numerals. — DCXXXIX
2. What fraction of the square is
   a shaded — a $\frac{5}{8}$
   b unshaded? — b $\frac{3}{8}$
3. Find the total of 79p, 41p and 85p. — £2.05
4. Write as 24-hour clock times.
   a 5 minutes to 9 in the morning — a 08:55
   b 10 minutes past 10 in the evening — b 22:10
5. By how many metres is 2km less than 2.35km? — 350m
6. Round 10.47 to the nearest whole number. — 10
7. What is the cost of 2m 10cm at 40p per metre? — 84p
8. By how many kilograms is $1\frac{1}{2}$kg greater than 350g? — 1.15kg
9. Find the total cost of 100 balloons at 7p each. — £7.00
10. What is the value in millilitres of the digit underlined in 7.360l? — 60ml
11. By how much is the total of seven 10ps and three 5ps less than £1? — 15p
12. Write in digits to the nearest 100 twenty thousand nine hundred and six. — 20 900

C | Answer

1. How many packets each containing 100 cards can be made from thirteen thousand cards? — 130
2. Find the change from £1 after paying for three oranges at 29p each. — 13p
3. $\frac{1}{7}$ of the mass of a container is 600g. Find its total mass in kilograms. — 4.2kg
4. ABC is an isosceles triangle. Find the size in degrees of the
   a angle at B — a 54°
   b angle at C. — b 54°
5. Three bottles contain 1.3l, 0.9l and 0.5l. Find in millilitres the mean average of these quantities. — 900ml
6. A bus journey takes 47min. If a bus leaves at 09:50, at what time does it arrive? — 10:37
7. garden area 480m² 40m | Find the width of the garden. — 12m
8. The population of a town is 59 609. Write this number to the nearest 1000. — 60 000
9. The bus fare for a child is half that of an adult. Find the total fares for two adults and four children if a full fare is 54p. — £2.16
10. On a map each 1mm represents 50m in real life. What length does a line measuring 8mm on the map represent? — 400m
11. What number is 17 less than 7? — −10
12. Which shape has the greater perimeter and by how many centimetres? — square by 2cm

square 8cm | rectangle 6cm 9cm

A | Answer

1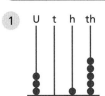
U t h th

Write in words as a decimal the number shown on the abacus.

<u>three point zero one five</u>

2 100 × ▦ = 10 000 | <u>100</u>

3 2.8km – 300m = ▦ km | <u>2.5km</u>

4 74p × 8 = £▦ | <u>£5.92</u>

5 0.2 × 6 = | <u>1.2</u>

6 0.065l = ▦ ml | <u>65ml</u>

7 $\frac{1}{6}$ of £4.80 = ▦ p | <u>80p</u>

8 47 + 53 + 4000 = | <u>4100</u>

9 0.75min = ▦ s | <u>45s</u>

10 42 – 15 = ▦ × 3 | <u>9</u>

11 3kg + 90g = ▦ kg | <u>3.09kg</u>

12 0.4 + 0.7 = | <u>1.1</u>

B | Answer

1 Increase 240 by $\frac{1}{3}$ of 60. | <u>260</u>

2 13 out of 25 = ▦ out of 100 | <u>52</u>

3 Find the change from £3.00 after spending £2.19. | <u>81p</u>

4 From twelve thousand take nine hundred and forty. | <u>11 060</u>

5 6 times 85cm = ▦ m | <u>5.1m</u>

6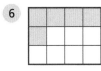
What fraction of the rectangle is

a shaded | a $\frac{5}{12}$

b unshaded? | b $\frac{7}{12}$

7 How many millimetres are there in 3.07m? | <u>3070mm</u>

8 How many times is 250g contained in $5\frac{1}{2}$ kg? | <u>22</u>

9 Reduce $\frac{70}{100}$ to a fraction in its lowest terms. | $\frac{7}{10}$

10 What is the cost of 100g at 85p per $\frac{1}{2}$ kg? | <u>17p</u>

11 A square has sides 30cm long. Find

a its perimeter | a <u>120cm</u>

b its area. | b <u>900cm²</u>

12 Share $100 equally among eight people. How much each? | <u>$12.50</u>

C | Answer

1 Divide 1655 by 100 and write the answer to the nearest whole number. | <u>17</u>

2 Simplifying your answer, write what fraction of the dots is

a white | a $\frac{1}{3}$

b purple. | b $\frac{2}{3}$

3 Plums are priced at three for 35p. How many can be bought for £2.10? | <u>18</u>

4 The mass of a box of books is 3.5kg. The mass of the box is 600g. Find the mass of the books in kilograms. | <u>2.9kg</u>

5 Sasmita lives 20.3km from her place of work. How many kilometres does she travel in a five-day week if she makes a return journey each day? | <u>203km</u>

6 Omar's date of birth is 30.08.94. What will be his age in years on 1 September 2020? | <u>26yr</u>

7 On a coordinate grid point A is at (3,4) but it is then moved two squares to the right and one square down. What are its new coordinates? | (5 , 3)

8 How many days would a 200ml bottle of milk last if two kittens were fed 5ml each four times a day? | <u>5</u>

9 15 × 17 = 255. Write the answers to

a 150 × 170 | a <u>25 500</u>

b 1.5 × 17. | b <u>25.5</u>

10 Find the cost at £5.70 per metre of

a 10cm | a <u>57p</u>

b 30cm. | b <u>£1.71</u>

11 A road on a map measured 4.5cm which represented a distance of 45km. What distance does 1mm on the map represent? | <u>1km</u>

12
a Name the shape. | a <u>parallelogram</u>

b Find its perimeter. | b <u>50cm</u>

c Find ∠ A. | c <u>55°</u>

A

		Answer
1	$2083 - 80 =$	2003
2	$6 + \frac{7}{10} + \frac{5}{1000} =$	6.705
3	$2050mm = \blacksquare m$	2.05m
4	$3h - 25min = \blacksquare min$	155min
5	six 2ps + five 5ps + three 10ps =	67p
6	$78.5 \div 100 =$	0.785
7	$\frac{4}{5} = \frac{\blacksquare}{100}$	$\frac{80}{100}$
8	$0.5l - 345ml = \blacksquare ml$	155ml
9	$27 + 18 = \blacksquare \times 5$	9
10	$1.8kg \div 3 = \blacksquare g$	600g
11	$\frac{2}{3}$ of £3.60 =	£2.40
12	$\angle A = \blacksquare °$	30°

B

		Answer
1	Write as a decimal the total of eleven plus twenty-six thousandths.	11.026
2	Find a number which when multiplied by itself gives as the answer	
	a 64	a 8
	b 49.	b 7
3	What is left after taking 17p from four 20ps?	63p
4	Write the decimal fraction which is equal to $\frac{3}{20}$.	0.15
5	How many minutes from 10.55 a.m. to 12.30 p.m.?	95min
6	By how many metres is 1.4km longer than 1250m?	150m
7	Find the difference between the largest and smallest of these decimals. 3.4 3.401 3.41	0.01
8	What is left over when 68p is divided by 7?	5p
9	Multiply 4.05kg by 100.	405kg
10	Find the mean of these lengths. 5.4cm 4.6cm 3.5cm	4.5cm
11	What number is represented by CM in Roman numerals? Write your answer in digits.	900
12	How many times is 260.6 greater than 2.606?	100

C

		Answer
1	Increase forty thousand by six hundred and three. Write the answer in digits.	40 603
2	Multiply the product of 8 and 7 by 101.	5656
3	How many less than 578 335 is the number	
	a 8334	a 570 001
	b 70 305?	b 508 030
4	Find the total of 285 056 and 13 501.	298 557
5	A box contains 10 bottles of shampoo each having a mass of 223g. Find the total mass to the nearest $\frac{1}{2}$kg allowing 230g for the box.	2.5kg or $2\frac{1}{2}$kg
6	By how many hundredths is 0.82 more than $\frac{4}{5}$?	2 hundredths
7	<table><tr><td>250g</td><td>100g</td></tr><tr><td>62p</td><td>25p</td></tr></table> The prices of two different packets of jelly are given. How much is saved by buying the larger packets when purchasing 500g of jelly?	1p
8	Round each of these numbers to the nearest whole number.	
	a 5.5	a 6
	b 199.71	b 200
	c 9.49	c 9
9	Which two of these fractions are each equal to $\frac{5}{6}$? $\frac{15}{18}$ $\frac{16}{20}$ $\frac{10}{15}$ $\frac{20}{24}$	$\frac{15}{18}$ $\frac{20}{24}$
10	SE is halfway between S and E. A ship sails east from port and then turns SE. Find the angle marked x.	135°
11	A rectangle measures 8cm by 6cm. What is the length of the sides of a square which has the same perimeter?	7cm
12	Find these measurements of the shaded triangle.	
	a the base	a 14cm
	b the height	b 8cm

A | Answer

1. $\frac{1}{4}$ of ten thousand = — **2500**
2. $6 \times 0 \times 9 \times 3 =$ — **0**
3. $0.9 + 0.1 =$ — **1**
4. $0.7 \times 2 =$ — **1.4**
5. $1632 \div 4 =$ — **408**
6. £5.00 – eight 5ps = £ ▨ — **£4.60**
7. $\frac{35}{100} = \frac{▨}{20}$ — **$\frac{7}{20}$**
8. 400g + ▨ g = 0.75kg — **350g**
9. 2h 25min + 50min = — **3h 15min**
10. 3.5km – 2900m = ▨ m — **600m**
11. Write 1005 using Roman numerals. — **MV**
12.

Angle $x = ▨°$ — **82°**

Angle $y = ▨°$ — **98°**

B | Answer

1. Find the product of 0.4 and 9. — **3.6**
2. What is the answer in grams when 24.5kg is divided by 100? — **245g**
3. From 50 take 0.01. — **49.99**
4. After Christmas Day, how many days are there before New Year's Day? — **6**
5. Find the total of six 20ps and seven 10ps. — **£1.90**
6. Write 0.05 as a fraction with the numerator 1. — **$\frac{1}{20}$**
7. Which of these numbers will divide into 81 without a remainder?

| 2 | 3 | 5 | 6 | 9 |

— **3   9**
8. Find the cost of 3.5l at 26p per $\frac{1}{2}$l. — **£1.82**
9. Which of these decimal fractions is equal to $\frac{3}{4}$?

| 0.7 | 0.65 | 0.75 |

— **0.75**
10. The length of a line is 15.6cm. Find half its length in millimetres. — **78mm**
11. $5.4 \div 6 = 0.9$. Write the answer to

a $0.54 \div 6$ — **a 0.09**

b $0.054 \div 6$. — **b 0.009**
12. Two angles in a triangle added together make 124°. Find the third angle. — **56°**

C | Answer

1. Find the number which is equal to $(9 \times 10^2) + 6$. — **906**
2. How many 4p sweets can be bought for £6.00? — **150**
3. Find in metres the length of ribbon required to make 200 pieces each 8.3cm long. — **16.6m**
4. How much greater than 582 482 is the number 884 492? — **302 010**
5. Midday temperatures on three consecutive days are 17°C, 15°C and 19°C. Find the mean temperature. — **17°C**
6. 1l of water has a mass of 1kg. Find the volume in litres of the water in a bottle if the water has a mass of 780g. — **0.78l**
7. An article priced at £4.20 was sold in a sale at a reduction of $\frac{1}{3}$. Find the sale price. — **£2.80**
8. On the chart each smiley face ☺ represents 50 pupils at a local school. How many pupils attend the school? — **850**

☺☺☺☺☺☺☺☺☺☺☺☺☺☺☺☺☺

9. William found the mass of 10 shuttlecocks to be 95g. Find the mass in kilograms of 100 shuttlecocks. — **0.95kg**
10.

ABC is an equilateral triangle. Find

a its perimeter in centimetres — **a 25.8cm**

b the size of the angles at B and C. — **b 60°**
11. Yasmin went shopping with a £5 note in her purse. She had left two 50ps, one 10p and six 2ps. How much had she spent? — **£3.78**
12.

Find the area of

a the rectangle — **a 108cm²**

b each of the triangles. — **b 54cm²**

21

A | Answer

1. $20\,000 = 20 \times 10 \times$ ▨ — **100**
2. $0.817 = 8$ tenths + ▨ thousandths — **17** thousandths
3. $57 \times 70 =$ — **3990**
4. $0.3 \times 6 =$ — **1.8**
5. $24 - (18 \times 0) =$ — **24**
6. $£20.36 =$ ▨ 10ps + 6p — **203 10ps**
7. $\frac{4}{5} - \frac{1}{2} =$ — **$\frac{3}{10}$**
8. $65\text{ml} \times 100 =$ ▨ l — **6.5l**
9. $2.6\text{cm} + 3.9\text{cm} =$ ▨ mm — **65mm**
10. $£$ ▨ $\times 9 = £40.50$ — **£4.50**
11. $1.5\text{kg} - 280\text{g} =$ ▨ g — **1220g**
12. $0.9 + 0.9 =$ — **1.8**

B | Answer

1. Write as a decimal 1035 thousandths. — **1.035**
2. Approximate 59.7p to the nearest 1p. — **60p**
3. a $\frac{9}{10} = \frac{▨}{100}$ — **a $\frac{90}{100}$**
   b Write the fraction as a decimal. — **b 0.9**
4. Which two of these angles when added together make two right angles?
   | 67° | 103° | 87° | 113° |
   — **67°   113°**
5. How many times 0.48 is 480? — **1000**
6. Find in millimetres the value of the digit underlined.
   7.07<u>5</u>m — **5mm**
7. 9 out of 25 = ▨ out of 100 — **36**
8. How much change out of a £5 note after spending £1.46? — **£3.54**
9. $\frac{1}{2}$ kg of tomatoes costs 80p. Find the cost of 100g. — **16p**
10. What fraction of $\frac{1}{4}$ l is 150ml? — **$\frac{3}{5}$**
11. Which of these fractions is between one-half and one-quarter in size?
   | $\frac{3}{5}$ | $\frac{2}{3}$ | $\frac{7}{10}$ | $\frac{3}{8}$ |
   — **$\frac{3}{8}$**
12. 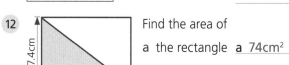 Find the area of
   a the rectangle — **a 74cm²**
   b the shaded triangle. — **b 37cm²**

C | Answer

1. How many bottles each holding $\frac{1}{4}$ l can be filled from $7\frac{1}{2}$ l? — **30**
2. A packet of 100 sheets of paper costs £2.30. Find the cost of 150 sheets. — **£3.45**
3. Take the least of these decimal fractions from the greatest.
   | 0.84 | 0.9 | 0.865 | 0.897 |
   — **0.06**
4. Lauren swims 15 lengths of the pool which is 20m long. How many metres short of $\frac{1}{2}$ km does she swim? — **200m**
5. 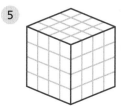 The large cube is made from a number of centimetre cubes.
   a How many centimetre cubes are there? — **a 64**
   b $4^3 =$ ▨ — **b 64**
6. Ryan saved 60p which was $\frac{5}{6}$ of his pocket money. How much was all his pocket money? — **72p**
7. 2.8kg of coffee was put into 10 packets of equal mass. How many grams of coffee were there in each packet? — **280g**
8. Find the size in degrees of ∠ A — **145°**
   ∠ B — **35°**
   ∠ C. — **35°**
9. The total cost of two full-price tickets and one half-price ticket was £55. Find the cost of
   a one full-price ticket — **a £22**
   b one half-price ticket. — **b £11**
10. What is the area in m² of a rectangular path which is 29m long and 50cm wide? — **$14\frac{1}{2}$m²**
11. Emma ran 9.875km in an afternoon. Round this distance to the nearest
   a kilometre — **a 10km**
   b tenth of a kilometre. — **b 9.9km**
12. Find a the perimeter of the shape — **a 34cm**
   b its area. — **b 44cm²**

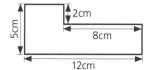

22

A

		Answer
1	$1200 \div 30 =$	40
2	$7p + 5p + 8p + 25p =$	45p
3	$(7 \times 9) - (8 + 5) =$	50
4	$\frac{6}{25} = \frac{\blacksquare}{100}$	$\frac{24}{100}$
5	$900g + 500g = \blacksquare kg$	1.4kg
6	$4.908 = 4 + \frac{9}{10} + \frac{\blacksquare}{1000}$	$\frac{8}{1000}$
7	$£0.86 - 19p = \blacksquare p$	67p
8	$2km - 540m = \blacksquare m$	1460m
9	$0.09 + 0.06 =$	0.15
10	$250ml \times 6 = \blacksquare l$	1.5l
11	$2m\ 80cm \div 4 = \blacksquare cm$	70cm
12	$180° - (63° + 57°) =$	60°

B

		Answer
1	Write as a decimal the total of 200, 6, $\frac{7}{10}$ and $\frac{9}{1000}$.	206.709
2	From the product of 7 and 9 take their sum.	47
3	Write as a fraction and simplify	
	a 9 out of 30	a $\frac{3}{10}$
	b 24 out of 40.	b $\frac{3}{5}$
4	How many days altogether are there in the months of April and May?	61
5	Find in grams the value of the digits underlined. 4.0<u>75</u>kg	75g
6	What must be added to 9.45 to make 10?	0.55
7	Change to decimal fractions.	
	a $\frac{27}{50}$	a 0.54
	b $\frac{9}{20}$	b 0.45
8	$\angle A = \angle B$ Find the size of each angle. 130°	25°
9	Divide £2.75 by 10 and write the answer to the nearest penny.	28p
10	Find the cost of 1.2m of tape at 40p per metre.	48p
11	Take 6 thousandths from 0.897.	0.891
12	Find in centimetres the perimeter of an equilateral triangle, the sides of which measure 27mm.	8.1cm

C

		Answer
1	By how many is 8^2 greater than 3^3?	37
2	Approximate 25928	
	a to the nearest 1000	a 26000
	b to the nearest 100.	b 25900
3	Find the date which is nine days after 26 September.	5 October
4	Round 3.52 to the nearest whole number.	4
5	What is the difference in millilitres between the largest and smallest of these quantities? $\frac{1}{2}l$ 450ml $\frac{3}{5}l$ 620ml	170ml

6 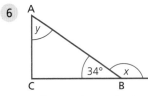 ABC is a right-angled triangle. Find in degrees

		Answer
	a the angle marked x	a 146°
	b the angle marked y.	b 56°
7	A length of plastic strip 54cm long is cut into two pieces so that one is five times as long as the other. What is the length of each piece?	45cm 9cm
8	George spent €80 which was $\frac{2}{5}$ of his savings. How much in savings did he have to begin with?	€200
9	On a coordinate grid point A is at (2, 0) but it is then moved three squares to the right and one square up. What are its new coordinates?	(5 , 1)
10	A 5p coin has a mass of 3.25g. Find in grams the mass of forty 5ps.	130g
11	A circular tin has a diameter of 6.4cm. What is a the length and b the width of the smallest rectangular tray which would contain a single row of 8 tins?	a 51.2cm b 6.4cm
12	Hannah stopped for coffee at a café.	
	a How far from home was the café?	a 4km
	b At what time did she stop for coffee?	b 10:00

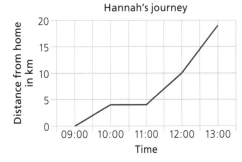

Hannah's journey

A | Answer

1. Write in digits the number forty thousand six hundred and five. — **40 605**

2. $(55 - 8) - (7 \times 0) =$ — **47**

3. 12 weeks = ▓ days — **84 days**

4. $\frac{3}{10}$ of $1\frac{1}{2}l =$ ▓ ml — **450ml**

5. Write as a decimal fraction.
   a $\frac{59}{100}$ — a **0.59**
   b $\frac{7}{100}$ — b **0.07**

6. $0.21 - 0.15 =$ — **0.06**

7. $5.405m =$ ▓ mm — **5405mm**

8. four 20ps + nine 2ps = £ ▓ — **£0.98**

9. a $0.45 = \frac{▓}{100}$ — a $\frac{45}{100}$
   b $0.08 = \frac{▓}{25}$ — b $\frac{2}{25}$

10. $208g + 1.5kg =$ ▓ kg — **1.708kg**

11. ▓ p × 6 = £4.56 — **76p**

12. $\frac{755}{7} =$ ▓ r ▓ — **107 r 6**

B | Answer

1.
   a What decimal fraction of the 100 small squares is shaded? — a **0.73**
   b Write this decimal fraction as a simple fraction. — b $\frac{73}{100}$

2. 47 out of 100 = 47 per cent (%). Write as a %
   a 79 out of 100 — a **79%**
   b 4 out of 100. — b **4%**

3. By how much is £15 more than fifteen 50ps? — **£7.50**

4. Find in millilitres the value of the digits underlined. 8.305l — **305ml**

5. Which year is MMXI? — **2011**

6. How many days are there between 28 November and 7 December? — **8**

7. 89% of a sum of money is spent. What percentage is left? — **11%**

8. Find the cost of 600g at 50p per $\frac{1}{2}$kg. — **60p**

9. The temperature fell 7°C from 4°C. What is the new temperature? — **−3°C**

10. Approximate
    a 10046 to the nearest 100 — a **10 000**
    b 3kg 370g to the nearest 0.5kg. — b **3.5kg**

11. Find the change from a £10 note after spending £7.62. — **£2.38**

12. The area of a rectangle is 47.5cm². Its width is 5cm. Find its length. — **9.5cm**

C | Answer

1. Write each of these fractions with a denominator of 100.
   a $\frac{3}{10}$ — a $\frac{30}{100}$
   b $\frac{2}{5}$ — b $\frac{40}{100}$
   c $\frac{1}{25}$ — c $\frac{4}{100}$

2. A school was built in 1902. For how many years will it have been in use by the year 2020? — **118yr**

3. What decimal fraction is equal to
   a 57% — a **0.57**
   b 8%? — b **0.08**

4. How many packets each containing 365g can be made from $36\frac{1}{2}$kg? — **100**

5. Write the next two decimal numbers in this sequence.
   1.75, 2.0, 2.25, ▓, ▓ — **2.5 2.75**

6. Prices in a shop were increased by $\frac{1}{3}$. Find the new price of articles which cost
   a 48p — a **64p**
   b 84p. — b **£1.12**

7. From a watering can holding 10l of water, 2.75l are poured on the plants. Find in litres and millilitres the quantity which remains. — **7l 250ml**

8. The sides of the cube each measure 5cm. Find the area of
   a one face — a **25cm²**
   b all the faces. — b **150cm²**

9. The mean of eight numbers is 12. Find the sum of the eight numbers. — **96**

10. 10 tennis balls cost $8.40. Find the cost of three tennis balls. — **$2.52**

11. 30l of orange squash is made by mixing 1 part concentrate with 4 parts water. Find the volume of
    a concentrate — a **6l**
    b water. — b **24l**

12. The path round the lawn is 1m wide. Find the area of the lawn. — **130m²**

Mental Arithmetic 4 Answers

A | Answer

1. 50 000 = 500 × ▓ — 100
2. (27 ÷ 3) = (▓ ÷ 7) — 63
3. a $\frac{1}{2}$ = ▓ out of 100 — a 50
   $\frac{1}{2}$ = ▓% — 50%
   b $\frac{1}{4}$ = ▓ out of 100 — b 25
   $\frac{1}{4}$ = ▓% — 25%
4. $1\frac{1}{2} - \frac{7}{10}$ = — $\frac{8}{10}$ or $\frac{4}{5}$
5. $5\frac{1}{2}$ min = ▓ s — 330s
6. 0.7 × 5 = — 3.5
7. £0.19 × 6 = — £1.14
8. $\frac{17}{20} = \frac{▓}{100}$ = ▓% — $\frac{85}{100}$ = 85%
9. 4.385 − 4.325 = — 0.06
10. $\frac{2}{3}$ of 75p = — 50p
11. 850g × 4 = ▓ kg — 3.4kg
12. £4.20 = six 50ps + ▓ 20ps — 6 20ps

B | Answer

1. Which of these numbers are multiples of 8?

   | 36 | 48 | 60 | 72 |

   — 48   72

2. Write as a percentage. a $\frac{63}{100}$ — a 63%
   b 0.07 — b 7%
3. Write four hundred and two thousand, one hundred and seven in digits. — 402 107
4. Find the cost of 750g at 48p per kilogram. — 36p
5. What must be added to £4.74 to make £6.00? — £1.26
6. Write in 24-hour clock time a quarter of an hour earlier than 23:10. — 22:55
7. Find the area of the right-angled triangle. 6cm 10.5cm — 31.5cm²
8. In a class 36% of the children were boys. What percentage were girls? — 64%
9. 360° − (80° + 75° + 120°) = ▓° — 85°
10. Find to the nearest penny $\frac{1}{8}$ of 95p. — 12p
11. Find the mean of these volumes.

    | 650ml | 800ml | 350ml |

    — 600ml
12. hexagon — What is the perimeter in centimetres of a regular hexagon each side of which measures 58mm? — 34.8cm

C | Answer

1. Write these decimal fractions as percentages.
   a 0.3 — a 30%
   b 0.07 — b 7%
   c 0.84 — c 84%
2. Leah had in her purse three 50ps, two 20ps and two 5ps. She spent £1.17. How much had she left? — 83p
3. Write the product of 0.007 and 4. — 0.028
4. What is the value of 1% of
   a £1 — a 1p
   b 1kg? — b 10g
5. The diagram represents a length of 72m. Find the length represented by the shaded part. — 27m

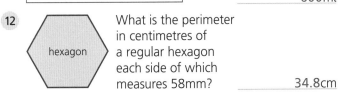

6. Shahid spends 38% of his pocket money on bus fares and 24% on books. What percentage of his money remains? — 38%
7. 1p has a mass of 3.56g. Find the mass in kilograms of £10 of 1p coins. — 3.56kg
8. 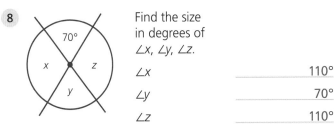 Find the size in degrees of ∠x, ∠y, ∠z.
   ∠x — 110°
   ∠y — 70°
   ∠z — 110°
9. 20 bags of flour were bought for £10.80 and sold at 60p per bag. Find the profit after selling all the bags. — £1.20
10. Round each of these numbers to the nearest whole number.
    a $9\frac{7}{12}$ — a 10
    b 100.06 — b 100
    c 4.815 — c 5
11. Tom received 2p each time Megan received 3p. How much did they each receive from a total of £2.00?
    Tom — 80p
    Megan — £1.20
12. How many tiles each 20cm square are needed to cover this surface? — 125

1m   5m

25

Schofield & Sims

A

		Answer
1	Write in digits one hundred and four thousand.	104 000
2	£1.11 + 8p + 9p + 24p =	£1.52
3	0.35 = ▨ thousandths	350 thousandths
4	2.8l − 630ml = ▨ml	2l 170ml
5	350g × 5 = ▨kg	1.75kg
6	$\frac{57}{100}$ of £500 =	£285
7	7m 28cm ÷ 8 = ▨cm	91cm
8	297 + 103 = 40 × ▨	10
9	$1 - (\frac{3}{10} + \frac{2}{5}) =$	$\frac{3}{10}$
10	8 × 7 = ▨ × 0.1	560
11	$\frac{£14.42}{7} =$	£2.06
12	a $\frac{1}{4}$ = 0.25 = ▨%	a 25%
	b $\frac{3}{4}$ = 0.75 = ▨%	b 75%

B

		Answer
1	Write as decimal fractions. a $\frac{3}{20}$	a 0.15
	b $\frac{8}{25}$	b 0.32
2	What is the difference in grams between $1\frac{3}{4}$kg and 950g?	800g
3	What length when divided by 6 is equal to 2m 50cm?	15m
4	The three angles of a triangle each measure 60°. Describe the triangle according to	
	a its angles	a acute-angled
	b its sides.	b equilateral
5	Find the value of	
	a 50% of 650	a 325
	b 25% of £0.72.	b 18p
6	How many times is 200ml contained in 2.8l?	14
7	Approximate to the nearest centimetre.	
	a 20.3cm	a 20cm
	b 79mm	b 8cm
8	Write 2017 using Roman numerals.	MMXVII
9	Find the length in metres which is equal to the digits underlined. 6.5<u>35</u>km	35m
10	At 75p per $\frac{1}{2}$kg find the cost of	
	a 100g	a 15p
	b 300g.	b 45p
11	Find in centimetres the perimeter of a rectangle which is 65mm long and 30mm wide.	19cm
12	a 0.1 = ▨%	a 10%
	b 0.4 = ▨%	b 40%

C

		Answer
1	18% of the people at a cinema were men, 39% were women and the rest were children. What percentage were children?	43%
2	Katie went on holiday on 29 July and returned on 7 August. For how many days was she on holiday?	10
3	Josh saved $\frac{1}{4}$ of his pocket money and spent $\frac{1}{2}$ of the remainder. What fraction did he spend?	$\frac{3}{8}$
4	The population of a small town was ten thousand. 50% of the people were under the age of 25. How many was that?	5000
5	What is the length in centimetres of the longest straight line that can be drawn inside this circle?	10.8cm
6	50% of a sum of money was £7.00. Find the whole sum of money.	£14
7	How many packets each containing 0.2kg can be made from 35kg?	175
8	A milkshake contains 7 parts of milk and 1 part of syrup. How many millilitres of each are required to make 2l?	1750ml 250ml
9	Kai's walking pace measures 60cm. How many metres has he walked after taking 50 paces?	30m
10	The mass of 120kg of dry sand is increased when wet by 10%. Find its mass when wet.	132kg
11	A scooter costing £25 is reduced by $\frac{1}{20}$. Find	
	a the price reduction	a £1.25
	b the new price.	b £23.75
12	Find the area of	
	a the front	a 72cm²
	b the end	b 31.5cm²
	c the bottom of the box.	c 112cm²

A | Answer

1) $6009 + \blacksquare = 8000$ — 1991
2) £3.75 + £3.75 + £3.75 + £3.75 = — £15.00
3) $\frac{7}{20}$ of £2.00 = $\blacksquare$p — 70p
4) $16\frac{2}{3} = \frac{\blacksquare}{3}$ — $\frac{50}{3}$
5) 19min + $\blacksquare$h $\blacksquare$min = 3h — 2h 41min
6) $\frac{11}{25} = \frac{\blacksquare}{100} = \blacksquare$% — $\frac{44}{100} = 44\%$
7) £2.00 – (78p + 30p) = $\blacksquare$p — 92p
8) $\frac{3}{10}$ of 1m 80cm = $\blacksquare$cm — 54cm
9) $0.05 \times 8 =$ — 0.4
10) $\frac{2kg\ 400g}{5} = \blacksquare$g — 480g
11) a $0.7 = \blacksquare$% — a 70%
    b $0.9 = \blacksquare$% — b 90%
12) $0.09 \times 12 =$ — 1.08

B | Answer

1) [grid with shaded squares] Write as a fraction, in its lowest terms, and then as a percentage, the part of the square which is
   a shaded — a $\frac{1}{5}$ 20%
   b unshaded. — b $\frac{4}{5}$ 80%

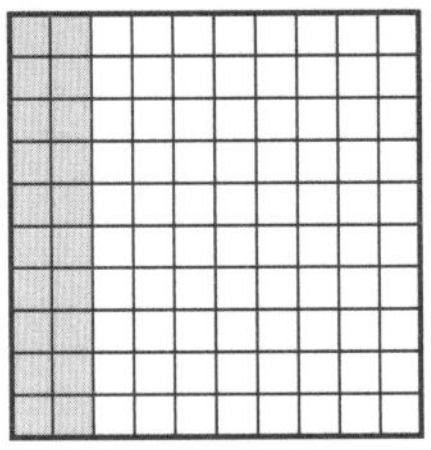

2) How many right angles are there in 270°? — 3

3) By what length is 50.4km longer than $47\frac{1}{2}$km? — 2.9km

4) Increase £3.70 by 10%. — £4.07

5) How many millilitres must be added to 3050ml to make $3\frac{1}{4}$l? — 200ml

6) $\frac{1}{4}$ of a sum of money is 79p. What is 50% of the money? — £1.58

7) Round 3.595 to the nearest tenth. — 3.6

8) Write as a fraction and simplify.
   a 20% — a $\frac{1}{5}$
   b 2% — b $\frac{1}{50}$

9) Approximate to the nearest $\frac{1}{2}$kg.
   a 7.65kg — a $7\frac{1}{2}$kg
   b 3850g — b 4kg

10) Find the product of 0.2 and 0.3. — 0.06

11) a Write 20% as a decimal fraction. — a 0.2
    b What is 20% of one thousand? — b 200

12) Use the formula A = lb to find the area of a rectangle when l = 16.5 cm and b = 9 cm. — 148.5cm²

C | Answer

1) Find the profit on a scarf which was bought for £8.35 and sold for £10. — £1.65

2) Two angles of a triangle each measure 78°.
   a Name the triangle. — a isosceles
   b Find the third angle. — b 24°

3) The line has been drawn to a scale 1mm to 10m. What distance in metres does it represent? — 780m
   |←——————— 7.8cm ———————→|

4) 40% of a sum of money is £36. Find
   a 10% of the sum of money — a £9
   b the whole sum of money. — b £90

5) [pentagon drawn in circle with shaded central angle]
   a Name the regular shape drawn in the circle. — a pentagon
   b What is the size of the angle shaded at the centre? — b 72°

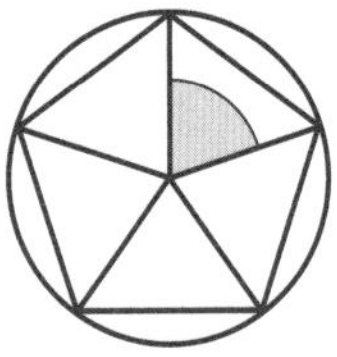

6) A bus runs every 35min starting at 07:40. At what time does the third bus leave? — 08:50

7) How many chocolates at three for 20p can be bought for £3.80? — 57

8) Write the coordinates of the point (2, 5) when it is reflected in the line $x = 4$. — (6 , 5)

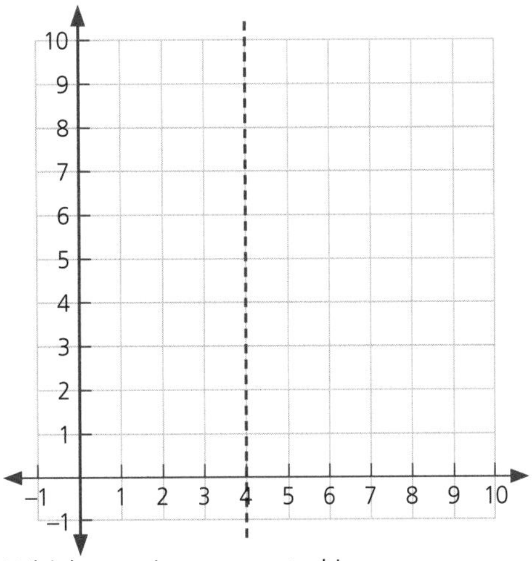

[coordinate grid, y-axis labelled 1 to 10, x-axis labelled −1 to 10, with dashed vertical line at x = 4]

9) Which year is represented in Roman numerals as MCMLXXXIV? — 1984

10) 0.5kg of mushrooms cost £1.20. What is the cost of   a 100g — a £0.24
                                                         b 0.9kg? — b £2.16

11) This shape is built from centimetre cubes. Find its dimensions.
    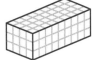
    a length — a 9cm
    b width — b 4cm
    c height — c 3cm

12) How many centimetre cubes are used to build the block? — 108

A

		Answer
1	$10^3 = 10 \times 10 \times 10 =$ ▨	1000
2	$1100 - 280 =$	820
3	$490g =$ ▨ kg	0.49kg
4	$0.14 - 0.07 =$	0.07
5	a $\frac{9}{100} =$ ▨ %	a 9%
	b $0.36 =$ ▨ %	b 36%
6	$3\frac{3}{4} - 2\frac{7}{8} =$	$\frac{7}{8}$
7	$9m \div 30 =$ ▨ cm	30cm
8	$£0.08 \times 7 = £$ ▨	£0.56
9	$60\% = \frac{▨}{5}$	$\frac{3}{5}$
10	175 seconds = ▨ min ▨ s	2min 55s
11	$0.073 =$ ▨ thousandths	73 thousandths
12	75% of 1.2kg = ▨ g	900g

B

		Answer
1	Find the total in litres of 700ml, 300ml and 450ml.	1.45l
2	How much greater than $\frac{1}{2}$ is	
	a 0.64	a 0.14
	b 0.502?	b 0.002
3	What is the time $\frac{3}{4}$h later than 23:20?	00:05
4	Find the cost of 50g at £1.40 per $\frac{1}{2}$kg.	14p
5	Round 0.249 to the nearest tenth.	0.2
6	Write each of the following as a an improper fraction and b a mixed number.	
	67 tenths	a $\frac{67}{10}$ b $6\frac{7}{10}$
	23 sixths	a $\frac{23}{6}$ b $3\frac{5}{6}$
7	Find the difference between $\frac{3}{4}$ of £1 and 0.8 of £1.	5p
8	How many grams are there in $\frac{1}{8}$ of 1kg?	125g
9	Write each of these percentages as a a decimal and b a simplified fraction.	
	80%	a 0.8 b $\frac{4}{5}$
	30%	a 0.3 b $\frac{3}{10}$
10	What is the value of x when 39 less than x is 76?	115
11	What percentage of £1.00 is	
	a 54p	a 54%
	b 6p?	b 6%
12	Find in m² the area of a rectangle 16.8m long and 50cm wide.	8.4m²

C

		Answer
1	Find the numbers between 30 and 50 which have both 4 and 6 as factors.	36 48
2	The mean amount saved by seven children was 83p. How much was saved altogether?	£5.81
3	How much further from home was Hannah at 12:00 than at 11:00?	6km

Hannah's journey — line graph: Distance from home in km (vertical axis, 0 to 20) against Time (horizontal axis, 09:00 to 13:00).

		Answer
4	The distance between two towns is 580km. If a map is drawn to a scale of 1cm to 100km what length in millimetres represents this distance?	58mm
5	Write as a fraction in its lowest terms.	
	a 100g of 400g	a $\frac{1}{4}$
	b 9km of 45km	b $\frac{1}{5}$
	c 500ml of $1\frac{1}{2}$l	c $\frac{1}{3}$
6	What is the temperature for 7°C below zero?	−7°C
7	Write the year 2014 using Roman numerals.	MMXIV
8	Find the missing divisor in this example. $\quad$ ▨$)\overline{8\ 7}$ with quotient 9 r 6	9
9	A bag contained an equal number of 10ps and 5ps to a total value of £4.50. How many coins were there of each kind?	30
10	By putting in a decimal point make the 7 in each number have the value of 7 thousandths.	
	a 2070	a 0.207
	b 67	b 0.067
11	Find the smallest amount of pence that can be added to £2.55 to make it divisible exactly by 7.	4p
12	A carpet 6.5m by 4m is fitted onto a floor to leave a border of 50cm wide.	
	Find a the length	a 7.5m
	b the breadth of the room.	b 5m

Mental Arithmetic 4 Answers

A

		Answer
1	$70\,000 = 10 \times 100 \times \blacksquare$	70
2	$4.505 = \blacksquare$ thousandths	4505 thousandths
3	3m 40cm + 1.8m = ▦m ▦cm	5m 20cm
4	$40 \times 2\frac{3}{4} =$	110
5	4.7kg + 2.4kg = ▦g	7100g
6	$\frac{1}{20} = \frac{\blacksquare}{100} = \blacksquare\%$	$\frac{5}{100} = 5\%$
7	$20\,000 + 800 + 6 =$	20806
8	$0.09 \times 6 =$	0.54
9	£70 ÷ 20 =	£3.50
10	40% of 900 =	360
11	350ml × 8 = ▦l	2.8l
12	100% of £3.86 =	£3.86

B

		Answer
1	By how many is 30090 less than forty thousand?	9910
2	Find the mean of these amounts. 47p, 62p, 13p and 18p	35p
3	What fraction of one hour is a 12min b 50min?	a $\frac{1}{5}$ b $\frac{5}{6}$
4	Find 5% of £4.00.	20p
5	How many degrees are there turning clockwise a from SE to W b from N to SW?	a 135° b 225°
6	Find the difference between the largest and smallest of these numbers. 2.202 2.02 2.22	0.2
7	What is the cost of 800ml at 90p per litre?	72p
8	By how many twelfths is $\frac{1}{4}$ less than $\frac{1}{3}$?	$\frac{1}{12}$
9	What percentage is a 20 of 200 b 250g of 1kg?	a 10% b 25%
10	Find the value of x when $\frac{x}{5} = 3$.	15
11	Find to the nearest pence $\frac{£7.87}{8}$	98p
12	What year is represented by MCMXLV?	1945

C

		Answer
1	What number when divided by 6 equals the product of 5 and 9?	270
2	How many hours and min are there from 09.40 to 13.25?	3h 45min
3	Of these quadrilaterals which has a four equal sides b only one pair of parallel sides? rectangle rhombus parallelogram trapezium	a rhombus b trapezium
4	20% of 700 children have school lunches. How many a have school lunches b bring a packed lunch from home?	a 140 b 560
5	How many sectors of the given size can be cut from the circle? (120°)	3
6	Seven packets of equal mass together have a mass of 4.55kg. Find in grams the mass of each packet.	650g
7	Which of these numbers are multiples of both 6 and 8? 16 24 30 36 42 48 64	24 48
8	One part of weed killer is mixed with 5 parts of water. How many millilitres of each are required to make 3l of weed killer?	500ml 2500ml
9	Charlie buys a bicycle for £80 and pays for it in weekly instalments of 10%. a For how many weeks does he pay? b How much is the weekly payment?	a 10 b £8
10	Put these decimals in ascending order. 0.75 0.7 0.57 0.8 0.5	0.5 0.57 0.7 0.75 0.8
11	A car travels 10km on 1l of petrol. How much petrol does the car use if it travels on average 450km daily for six days?	270l
12	a How many cm cubes fit exactly into the bottom of the box? (7cm, 15cm) b If the box is 3cm high, how many cm cubes are needed to fill it?	a 105 b 315

29

Write the numbers 1 to 20 down the side of a piece of paper.
Write alongside these numbers the **answers only** to the following questions.
Work as quickly as you can. Time allowed – **10 minutes**.

1 Write in words the number which is equal to 10^3. — one thousand

2 Aaliyah has saved £2, five 20ps, seven 10ps, six 5ps and eight 2ps.
By how much is the total less than £10? — £5.84

3 $385\,373 + 10\,505 =$ — 395 878

4 $\frac{7}{8}$ of a sum of money is 63p. Find the amount of all of the money. — 72p

5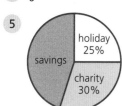

The diagram shows how Lucy spends her lottery winnings.
What percentage of the money is put into savings? — 45%

6 $59 \times 37 = 2183$. Write the answer to 0.59×37. — 21.83

7 What number is 10 more than −4? — 6

8 90% of 580 pupils went on a school trip. How many children remained at school? — 58

9 Find to the nearest kilometre the distance from Troup to Ling. — 24km

10 The width of a rectangular path is $\frac{1}{2}$m. Its area is 27.5m². Find its length. — 55m

11 Find the mass in kilograms and grams of 20% of 18kg. — 3kg 600g

12 How much less than $\frac{1}{2}$ is 0.494? — 0.006

13 In this parallelogram find in degrees the angle marked y. — 65°

14 Prices at a sale were reduced by 5%. How much is paid for a notebook priced at €1.80? — €1.71

15 The total of 7 numbers is 1428. What is the mean average of the numbers? — 204

16 Find to the nearest penny the cost of 1.5m of ribbon at £1.05 per metre. — £1.58

17 How many centimetre cubes are needed to fill the box? — 180

18 How many times greater than 0.03 is 30? — 1000

19 How many 6cm square tiles are required to cover a rectangular surface measuring
54cm long and 48cm wide? — 72

20 Write the year 1956 using Roman numerals. — MCMLVI

You will work through Progress Test 2 at **four** different times – once at the end of Section 2, then again after you have completed each of Section 3 Test 4, Test 8 and Test 12.

When you first complete the test:
a colour the first column to show the number of answers correct out of 20
b enter the date.

Each time you take the test, enter the result and the date in the marked columns.

	1st	2nd	3rd	4th
20				
19				
18				
17				
16				
15				
14				
13				
12				
11				
10				
9				
8				
7				
6				
5				
4				
3				
2				
1				
0				
date				

number of answers correct

A | Answer

1. Write in digits, two hundred and six thousand and forty. **206 040**

2. $4.008 = $ ▨ thousandths **4008 thousandths**

3. $39 \times 200 = $ **7800**

4. seventeen 20ps and six 10ps = £ ▨ **£4.00**

5. $0.1 - 0.05 = $ **0.05**

6. $7.045 \text{ km} = $ ▨km ▨m **7km 45m**

7. 10% of 3kg = ▨g **300g**

8. $\frac{2}{5}$ of £1.40 = ▨p **56p**

9. $450\text{ml} \times 8 = $ ▨l **3.6l**

10. a $\frac{7}{12} = \frac{21}{▨}$ a $\frac{21}{36}$

   b $\frac{27}{30} = \frac{▨}{10}$ b $\frac{9}{10}$

11. $\frac{3}{4}$h − 18min = ▨min **27min**

12. $\frac{£8.96}{7} = $ **£1.28**

B | Answer

1. Find the total of 17p, 34p and 29p. Write the answer as £s. **£0.80**

2. What fraction in its simplest form is 150ml to 1l? **$\frac{3}{20}$**

3. Approximate to the nearest whole number.

   a $9\frac{2}{3}$ a **10**

   b 24.06   b **24**

4. Find the cost of 5.2m at 40p per metre. **£2.08**

5. By how many is 99 060 less than one hundred thousand? **940**

6. Write the 24-hour clock time which is 16min later than 23:45. **00:01**

7. How many times is $\frac{3}{4}$ contained in $4\frac{1}{2}$? **6**

8. What percentage is

   a 3p of £1.00   a **3%**

   b 35cm of 1m?   b **35%**

9. Find the difference between 0.85l and 900ml. **50ml**

10. What mass in kilograms is 7 times 350g? **2.45kg**

11. Find the perimeter of a rectangle which measures 8.4cm by 5.9cm. **28.6cm**

12. $x \times 9 = $ 7m 200mm. Find the length in millimetres which is equal to x. **800mm**

C | Answer

1. How many hundredths must be added to 3.81 to make a total of 4? **19 hundredths**

2. A bottle holds 250ml of juice. How many bottles can be filled from 10l? **40**

3. Of the people attending a tennis match 57% were men, 29% were women and the remainder were children. What percentage were children? **14%**

4. A car travelled 300km at a speed of 60km per hour (km/h). How long did the journey take? **5h**

5. By how many pennies are seven 10ps greater than the total of eight 5ps and nine 2ps? **12p**

6. What fraction of the circle is

   a unshaded   a **$\frac{7}{12}$**

   b shaded?   b **$\frac{5}{12}$**

7. A metal strip is 20cm long. How many such strips can be cut from two lengths each 5m 60cm long? **56**

8. A bus arrived at the station at 18:23 but it was 35mins late due to heavy traffic. Find the scheduled arrival time. **17:48**

9. The price for $\frac{1}{2}$kg of carrots in four consecutive weeks was 36p, 32p, 28p, 24p. Find the mean price per $\frac{1}{2}$kg. **30p**

10. The average length of three pieces of wood is 13cm. Two of the pieces measure 12cm and 18cm. What is the length of the third piece? **9cm**

11. A map is drawn to a scale of 1cm to 1m. Express this scale

   a as a fraction   a **$\frac{1}{100}$**

   b as a ratio.   b **1:100**

12. Find in cm² the area of

   a the front   a **105cm²**

   b the bottom of the box.   b **157.5cm²**

A · Answer

1. Write in words the number 410 006.

   four hundred and ten thousand and six

2. 375m = ▢ km · 0.375km

3. 0.009 + 0.45 = · 0.459

4. 85ml × 100 = ▢ l · 8.5l

5. a 7% of £1.00 = ▢ p · **a** 7p

   b 7% of £6.00 = ▢ p · **b** 42p

6. $\frac{5}{8}$ of 72p = · 45p

7. 0.875kg = ▢ g · 875g

8. 108min = ▢ h ▢ min · 1h 48min

9. 634 ÷ 1000 = · 0.634

10. $0.08 × 30 = · $2.40

11. 0.2 − 0.17 = · 0.03

12. 25% of 150 = · 37.5 or $37\frac{1}{2}$

B · Answer

1. Write as a decimal the total of 10, $\frac{3}{10}$ and $\frac{17}{1000}$. · 10.317

2. Find the product of 7, 9 and 5. · 315

3. What is the cost of 750g at 48p per $\frac{1}{2}$kg? · 72p

4. By how many sixths is $\frac{2}{3}$ greater than $\frac{1}{2}$? · $\frac{1}{6}$

5. The strip is divided into three parts. What percentage of the whole is each part? · A 30% · B 50% · C 20%

A			B			C

6. Write in grams the value of the 7 in 6.875kg. · 70g

7. Find the number of days, not counting the first, from 21 June to 7 July. · 16 days

8. Decrease £3.50 by 20% · £2.80

9. Add together the largest and smallest of these numbers.

2.01	2.11	2.001	2.101

   · 4.111

10. By how many hundredths is 9.07 less than 10? · 93 hundredths

11. Write a £10.62 to the nearest £ · **a** £11

    b 3l 330ml to the nearest $\frac{1}{2}$l. · **b** $3\frac{1}{2}$l

12. Find in cm² the area of a rectangle 15cm long by 50mm wide. · 75cm²

C · Answer

1. Joe cycled 30km each day for a fortnight. How many kilometres did he cycle altogether? · 420km

2. Rose paid 46p with a £1 coin and received three coins as change. Name the three coins. · 50p 2p 2p

3. The circumference (the distance around the edge) of a wheel is 1m. How many times does the wheel turn in going 0.75km? · 750

4. In the number 28.0$\overset{y}{3}\overset{x}{8}$ how many times is the 8 marked x smaller than the 8 marked y? · 1000

5. 3m of cable cost £3.60. Find the cost of 15m. · £18.00

6. On a coordinate grid point A is at (5, 2) but it is then moved two squares to the left and one square down. What are its new coordinates? · (3 , 1)

7. A parcel has a mass of 1.8kg. Find the mass in grams of a parcel which is two-thirds of this mass. · 1200g

8.
16.1.13
18.4.13
17.7.12

   The dates of birth of three children are given.

   a By how many months is the oldest child older than the youngest? · **a** 9mth

   b In which year will the youngest child be 35 years old? · **b** 2048

9. 2.25l of milk are poured in equal amounts into five glasses. How many millilitres are there in each glass? · 450ml

10. A line about which a shape balances is called an axis of symmetry. Which of these shapes A, B, C or D has one axis of symmetry? · A

    A B C D

11. Rory received a gift of a £10 note. He spent £3. What % did he keep? · 70%

12. 8cm ... 10cm ... 6cm ... 15cm — Find the area of the shape in cm². · 122cm²

A

		Answer
1	$50 \times 10 \times 1000 =$	500 000
2	$1.2km - 900m = \blacksquare m$	300m
3	$48p \times 7 = £\blacksquare$	£3.36
4	$29 + 25 = 6 \times \blacksquare$	9
5	$5 - 3\frac{3}{8} =$	$1\frac{5}{8}$
6	75% of €10 =	€7.50
7	$3kg \div 8 = \blacksquare g$	375g
8	a $0.45 = \blacksquare \%$	a 45%
	b $\frac{11}{50} = \blacksquare \%$	b 22%
9	$400ml + 250ml + 500ml = \blacksquare l$	1.15l
10	$0.84 = \blacksquare$ thousandths	840 thousandths
11	eight 5ps + $\blacksquare$ 2ps = 60p	10 2ps
12	$70° + 38° + \blacksquare° = 180°$	72°

B

		Answer
1	Write in words the number 1 000 000.	one million
2	How much change from £4.00 after spending £3.26?	74p
3	What percentage of 2kg is 500g?	25%
4	Find the cost of 1m 30cm at 80p per metre.	£1.04
5	What is the difference in millimetres between 3.9cm and 4.6cm?	7mm
6	Divide the sum of 38 and 27 by 5.	13

7 Find the reflex angle at O.

Answer: 236°

		Answer
8	What is the time in hours and minutes from 10.15 a.m. to 12.05 p.m.?	1h 50min
9	How many times is 300ml contained in 1.8l?	6
10	The total mass of five parcels is 2kg 400g. Find the average mass of the parcels.	480g
11	What fraction in its simplest form is equal to	
	a 15%	a $\frac{3}{20}$
	b 4%?	b $\frac{1}{25}$
12	Find the answer to CMX – LIV and write the answer using Roman numerals.	DCCCLVI

C

		Answer
1	Faye wrote the total of £2.50, £3.50 and £2.75 as £9.25. By how much was her total wrong?	50p
2	Complete the set of square numbers between 10 and 101 by finding x and y. S = {16, 25, 36, x, 64, y, 100}	x 49
		y 81
3	1l of water has a mass of 1kg. Find the mass of 850ml of water.	850g
4	A plan is drawn to a scale of 1mm to 50m. What length in metres does a line measuring 5cm on the plan represent?	2500m

5 Write the part which is shaded

	Answer
a as a fraction	a $\frac{13}{20}$
b as a fraction with the denominator 100	b $\frac{65}{100}$
c as a decimal	c 0.65
d as a percentage.	d 65%

		Answer
6	Chloe gave a 50p and a 20p to pay for an item which cost 57p. How much change did she receive?	13p
7	A rectangle measures 10cm by 6cm. Find the length of another rectangle of the same area if its width is 4cm.	15cm
8	$18 \times 56 = 1008$. How many more than 1008 is 18×59?	54

9
The circumference of the wheel is 248cm. Find the distance travelled in metres in making 100 turns.

Answer: 248m

		Answer
10	The mass of a parcel is 10kg. 5% of its mass is for packing. Find in kilograms and grams the mass of the contents.	9kg 500g
11	10 muffins cost £6.28. Find to the nearest penny the cost of one muffin.	63p

12
Find the size in degrees of $\angle x$, $\angle y$, $\angle z$.

	Answer
$\angle x$	115°
$\angle y$	65°
$\angle z$	115°

A	Answer
1 2.5m + 43cm = ▢ cm	293cm
2 £0.96 = eight 2ps + ▢ 20ps	4 20ps
3 Write in digits $\frac{1}{2}$ million.	500 000
4 $\frac{4}{5}$ = ▢ %	80%
5 $\frac{5}{8}$ + $\frac{1}{2}$ + 2 =	$3\frac{1}{8}$
6 1.35l = ▢ ml	1350ml
7 150 ÷ 8 = ▢ r ▢	18 r 6
8 4.38 × 6 =	26.28
9 £1.94 − 86p = £ ▢	£1.08
10 5% of 300g =	15g
11 $\frac{9}{10}$ of £4.00 =	£3.60
12 1.05km + ▢ m = 2km	950m

B	Answer
1 Write as a decimal, fourteen units plus seventeen thousandths.	14.017
2 How many pennies remain when £1.11 is divided by 9?	3p
3 Find the product of 0.05 and 8.	0.4
4 What fraction in its simplest form is	
a 40min of 1 hour	a $\frac{2}{3}$
b 300ml of $\frac{1}{2}$ l?	b $\frac{3}{5}$
5 a Write the date which is 7 months later than 1 September 14.	a 1 April 15
b How many days are there in that month?	b 30
6 Find the cost of 1kg 200g at 50p per $\frac{1}{2}$ kg.	£1.20
7 a 20% of £4.50	a 90p
b 60% of £4.50	b £2.70
8 How many times greater than 3.04 is 3040?	1000
9 A car travels at 54km per hour. How far does it travel in 30min?	27km
10 Which of these angles are reflex angles? 105° 70° 190° 175° 210°	190° 210°
11 Approximate	
a 5050 to the nearest 100	a 5100
b 29 632 to the nearest 1000.	b 30 000
12 The area of a rectangle is 60m². Its length is 8m. Find the width of the rectangle.	7.5m

C	Answer
1 The heights of three children are 140cm, 160cm and 135cm. Find the average height in metres and centimetres.	1m 45cm
2 A car travels 170km on 20l of petrol. How many kilometres per litre?	8.5km
3 A letter was posted in Australia on 24 October and delivered in Britain on 4 November. For how many days was it in the post? Include the day of posting.	12 days
4 Three sweets cost 27p. Find the cost of seven sweets.	63p
5 Write each of these numbers so that the value of the digit 6 is 6 hundredths.	
a 306	a 3.06
b 463	b 0.463
c 2586	c 25.86
6 ABCD is a parallelogram and ∠ ABC is 55°. What is the size of	

	Answer
∠ ADC	55°
∠ DAB	125°
∠ BCD?	125°
7 A rectangular field 150m wide required 800m of fencing to enclose it. How long is the field?	250m
8 A 5p coin weighs 3.25g. By how many grams is the mass of a £5 bag of 5ps greater than $\frac{1}{4}$ kg?	75g
9 SALE Camera Was £87 Now 10% Off Find a the 10% reduction	a £8.70
b the new price.	b £78.30
10 A rectangular piece of paper with length 21cm and width 30cm is folded diagonally in half and cut. What is the area of each triangle produced?	315cm²
11 On a map the distance between two towns is 60mm. If the map was drawn to the scale 1cm to 5km, find the actual distance between the towns.	30km
12 a How many cm cubes are needed to fill the box?	a 240
b If the box were 4cm high, find its volume in cm³.	b 320cm³

Schofield & Sim

A

		Answer
1	$100 - 28 = 9 \times$ ▢	8
2	$250\,000 =$ ▢ million	$\frac{1}{4}$ million
3	$18p + 19p + 23p = £$ ▢	£0.60
4	$1.2m - 75cm =$ ▢ cm	45cm
5	$450g \times 6 =$ ▢ kg	2.7kg
6	a 10% of $840 =$	a 84
	b 30% of $840 =$	b 252
7	$£3.70 \div 8 =$ ▢ p r ▢ p	46p r 2p
8	$3min\ 50s =$ ▢ s	230s
9	$1 - \frac{3}{4} - \frac{1}{8} =$	$\frac{1}{8}$
10	$3.0 \times 0.8 =$	2.4
11	$3.050l +$ ▢ ml $= 4l$	950ml
12	a $0.55 =$ ▢ $\%$	a 55%
	b $\frac{1}{25} =$ ▢ $\%$	b 4%

B

		Answer
1	Which of these numbers are factors of 54?	
	4 5 6 7 8 9	6 9
2	How many 5ps are there in £3.65?	73 5ps
3	What is the average of 200ml, 250ml, 150ml and 120ml?	180ml
4	Write each of these scores as a percentage.	
	a 5 out of 25	a 20%
	b 16 out of 50	b 32%
5	How many metres are there in 1.65km?	1650m
6	Increase £50 by 25%.	£62.50
7	How many hours and minutes from 10.40 a.m. to 12.50 p.m.?	2h 10min
8	$\frac{7}{10}$ of 5m = 350cm. Find $\frac{3}{10}$ of 5m.	150cm
9	How many hundredths are there in three point zero four?	304 hundredths
10	200g cost 38p. Find the cost of $\frac{1}{2}$ kg.	95p
11	$635 \div 7$. Write the answer to the nearest whole number.	91

12

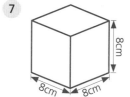

In this right-angled triangle, what is the size in degrees of the angle marked A?

60°

C

		Answer
1	Find the difference between the sum of 6 and 7 and the product of 6 and 7.	2
2	Which of these fractions are equivalent to 30%?	
	$\frac{3}{5}$ 0.03 $\frac{3}{10}$ $\frac{20}{50}$ 0.3	$\frac{3}{10}$ 0.
3	Caitlin has 25p and Billy has 41p. How much must Billy give to Caitlin so that they have equal amounts?	8
4	A jug when $\frac{3}{4}$ full holds 720ml. How many millilitres does it hold when it is	
	a $\frac{1}{8}$ full	a 120m
	b $\frac{3}{8}$ full?	b 360m
5	A train journey takes 1h 38min. If the train departs at 11:30 at what time does it arrive?	13:0
6	Oliver faces SW. In which direction is he facing if he turns	
	a 90° clockwise	a NW
	b 45° anticlockwise?	b S
7	a Find the area of one face.	a 64cm²
	b Find the area of all the faces of the cube.	b 384cm²
8	A customer paid 84p for 300g of grapes. Find the price for $\frac{1}{2}$ kg.	£1.40
9	Which of the following numbers do not change in value if the zeros are omitted?	
	0.158 0350 0.590 1.506	0.158 0.590
10	The perimeter of a rectangle is 54cm. Its length is 18cm. Find	
	a its width	a 9cm
	b its area.	b 162cm²
11	Find the smallest number which must be added to 403 to make it exactly divisible by 8.	5
12	What is the distance in cm from Y to Z?	12cm

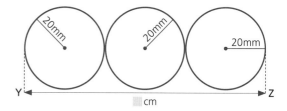

A | Answer

1. Write as a decimal $10 + \frac{8}{100} + \frac{3}{1000}$. — 10.083

2. 3.125l = ▢ ml — 3125ml

3. $\frac{3}{10}$ of £1.80 = ▢ p — 54p

4. 10% of twenty thousand = — 2000

5. 38mm + 26mm + 40mm = ▢ cm — 10.4cm

6. $10^2 - 4^3 =$ — 36

7. $0.02 \times 5 =$ — 0.1

8. $\frac{1}{2}$kg = 135g + ▢ g — 365g

9. $\frac{3}{4}$h $- \frac{2}{3}$h = ▢ min — 5min

10. 47p × 8 = £▢ — £3.76

11. 0.25 + ▢ = 0.365 — 0.115

12. $35 ÷ 4 =$ — $8.75

B | Answer

1. How many hundreds are there in thirty thousand seven hundred? — 307

2. 100 pencils cost £5.92. Find the cost of 25 pencils. — £1.48

3. By how many degrees does the temperature rise from –10°C to 4°C? — 14°C

4. Which of these numbers are multiples of both 6 and 8?

   | 16 | 24 | 36 | 54 | 72 |

   — 24   72

5. Find the mean of $2\frac{1}{4}$, $1\frac{3}{4}$ and $3\frac{1}{2}$. — $2\frac{1}{2}$

6. By how many grams is 750g less than 1kg 150g? — 400g

7. Write 35 eighths as

   a an improper fraction — a $\frac{35}{8}$

   b a mixed number. — b $4\frac{3}{8}$

8. 20% of a sum of money is 49p. Find 100% of the money. — £2.45

9. How many days are there in the seventh month of the year? — 31

10. Write as a fraction in its simplest form.

    a 15 out of 40 — a $\frac{3}{8}$

    b 28 out of 32 — b $\frac{7}{8}$

11. Approximate 17.85l to the nearest $\frac{1}{2}$ l. — 18l

12. Find in degrees.

    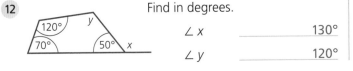

    ∠ x — 130°

    ∠ y — 120°

C | Answer

1. The approximate population of a city is forty thousand more than $\frac{1}{2}$ million. What is the approximate population? — 540 000

2. Jessica collected 50p in her money box. She has seventeen 1ps, nine 2ps and some 5ps. How many 5ps has she? — 3 5ps

3. 480 men, women and children went to a concert. From the diagram find how many

   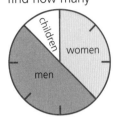

   a men — a 240

   b women — b 180

   c children — c 60

   were at the concert.

4. The perimeter of a regular octagon is 21.6cm. Find in millimetres

   a the length of one side — a 27mm

   b the length of a side of a regular hexagon of the same perimeter. — b 36mm

5. The price of a ticket was increased from 50p to 60p. What is the increase

   a as a fraction in its simplest form — a $\frac{1}{5}$

   b as a percentage of the original price? — b 20%

6. How many packets each containing 300g can be made from 2.5kg? How many grams are left? — 8 r 100g

7. Write using Roman numerals, the answer to LXIV × IX. — DLXXVI

8. A room is $1\frac{1}{4}$ times as long as it is wide. If the width is 6m find the area of the room. — 45m²

9. In the triangle ABC find

   ∠ ABC — 55°

   ∠ BAC — 70°

   ∠ ACB. — 55°

10. Lemonade is made from 3 parts water and 2 parts lemon juice.

    a What percentage of the mixture is water? — a 60%

    b Find the volume of lemon juice required to make 2l of lemonade. — b 800ml

11. Science Museum ADMISSION £3.40 half-price entry for children

    What is the total admission price for two adults and two children? — £10.20

12.

    The lawn measures 12m by 7m. The path around it is 1.5m wide. Find the area of the whole garden. — 150m²

A

			Answer
1	Write in digits $\frac{1}{10}$ of 1 million.		100 000
2	85g × 100 = ▦ kg		8.5kg
3	1.06 − 0.79 =		0.27
4	480mm = ▦ m		0.48m
5	$\frac{5}{6}$ of 30p =		25p
6	905 ÷ 100 =		9.05
7	a 1% of £3.00 = ▦ p	a	3p
	b 9% of £3.00 = ▦ p	b	27p
8	£0.04 × 50 =		£2.00
9	$\frac{3}{4}$h + 35min = ▦ h ▦ min		1h 20min
10	2.65l = ▦ ml		2650ml
11	19p + 7p + 5p + 8p = £ ▦		£0.39
12	$\frac{3}{4}$ × 8 =		6

B

			Answer
1	Write as a decimal the sum of 9 tenths and 37 thousandths.		0.937
2	Find the two missing numbers in this sequence. 70, 7, ▦, 0.07, ▦		0.7 0.007
3	What is the average of 15cm, $\frac{1}{4}$m and 17cm?		19cm
4	Increase £7.50 by 10%.		£8.25
5	By how many twelfths is $1\frac{5}{6}$ less than $2\frac{1}{4}$?		$\frac{5}{12}$
6	Write in 24-hour clock times.		
	a 18min before noon	a	11:42
	b $\frac{1}{2}$h after 7.57 p.m.	b	20:27
7	Find the difference between $\frac{1}{5}$ of 25 and $\frac{1}{3}$ of 45.		10
8	5% of a sum of money is £0.40. Find the whole amount.		£8.00
9	Approximate		
	a 10.25l to the nearest litre	a	10l
	b £439.87 to the nearest £.	b	£440
10	Find in millimetres the length of a line 15mm shorter than AB.		156mm

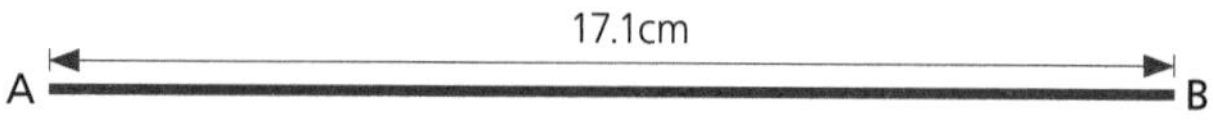

A ⟵———— 17.1cm ————⟶ B

11	What is the cost of 800g at 90p per kilogram?		72p
12	The area of a rectangle is $66\frac{1}{2}$cm². The width of the rectangle is 7cm. Find its length.		$9\frac{1}{2}$cm

C

			Answer
1	Write in words the number which is equal to $(3 × 10^3) + (6 × 10^2)$.		three thousand six hundred
2	There are 60 cards in a packet. There are 12 packets and 17 cards left over. How many cards are there altogether?		737
3	A bill for £4.23 is paid with a £5 note. Name the four coins given as change.	50p 20p	5p 2p
4	ABC is an isosceles triangle. Find the angle at B and the angle at A.		49° 82°

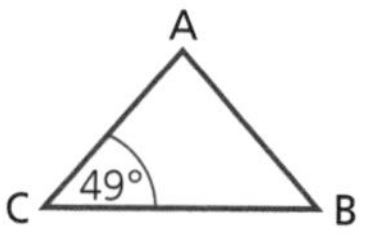

(triangle with A at top, angle 49° at C, B at bottom right)

5	How many years apart are these two years written in Roman numerals? MCMXLV MCMXXXIX Give your answer in digits.		6
6	A plank of wood 7.5m long is cut into two parts so that one part is four times as long as the other. Find the length of each part.		6m 1.5m

7		Train times		Which train, A or B, is the quicker and by how many minutes?		B by 8min

Train times	Depart	Arrive
A	10:45	12:35
B	16:18	18:00

8	The total mass of 12 parcels of equal mass is 5.4kg. Find the mass of		
	a four parcels in kilograms and grams	a	1kg 800g
	b one parcel in grams.	b	450g
9	The rectangle X has two axes of symmetry. How many axes of symmetry has		
	a rhombus Y	a	2
	b the equilateral triangle Z?	b	3

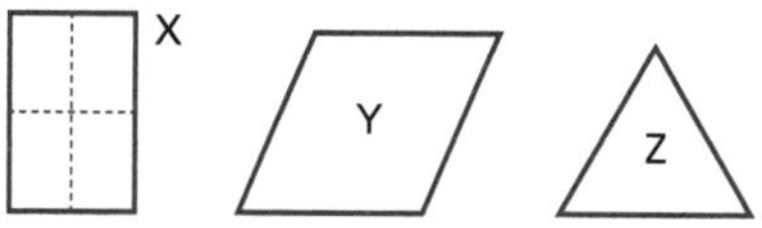

(rectangle X, rhombus Y, triangle Z)

10	The circumference of a wheel is 45cm. How many times will it turn in going 450m?		1000
11	By how much is it cheaper to pay for a coat priced at £25 with a discount of 10%, than with a discount of 8p per £1?		50p
12	The radius of this circle is 0.9 cm. Find the length of the line XY in mm.		18mm

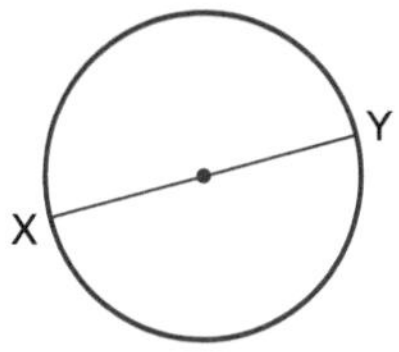

(circle with line XY through centre)

A — Answer

1. Write in digits 1.1 million. — 1 100 000
2. £0.81 = two 20ps + three 10ps + ▦ p — 11p
3. 8.07 × 6 = — 48.42
4. 1.8km + 450m = ▦ km ▦ m — 2km 250m
5. 50% of 1.9kg = ▦ g — 950g
6. 275 ÷ 7 = ▦ r ▦ — 39 r 2
7. $10^3 - 10^2 =$ — 900
8. a $\frac{3}{5}$ = ▦ % — a 60%
   b $\frac{9}{10}$ = ▦ % — b 90%
9. £10 − (2 × 46p) = £ ▦ — £9.08
10. $1\frac{3}{10} + \frac{2}{3} + \frac{7}{10} =$ — $2\frac{2}{3}$
11. 1.5l − ▦ ml = 600ml — 900ml
12. £0.17 × 8 = — £1.36

B — Answer

1. Find in degrees the reflex angle to
   a 85° — a 275°
   b 148°. — b 212°
2. How many 50g cans have a total mass of 2kg? — 40
3. Decrease £3.50 by 4%. — £3.36
4. Approximate
   a 9l 870ml to the nearest litre — a 10l
   b 3.56kg to the nearest $\frac{1}{2}$kg. — b $3\frac{1}{2}$kg
5. What was the date 6 months before 1 March 2000? — 1 September 1999
6. Divide nine hundred and seventy-two by nine. — 108
7. a 5% of £6.00 = ▦ p — a 30p
   b 15% of £6.00 = ▦ p — b 90p
8. How long would it take to travel 56km at a speed of 7km per hour? — 8h
9. Find the cost of 1.75l at 60p per litre. — £1.05
10. Divide a length of 48cm into two pieces so that one is twice as long as the other. — 32cm 16cm
11. What fraction in its lowest terms is
    a £27 of £36 — a $\frac{3}{4}$
    b £2.50 of £20? — b $\frac{1}{8}$
12. Find the area of the smallest square into which the circle can be fitted. (3.5cm) — 49cm²

C — Answer

1. There were 3500 spectators at a football match. 30% were women. How many women were there? — 1050
2. A bottle holds 300ml. Find in litres the contents of 12 bottles. — 3.6l
3. In the diagram there are 100 small squares. Find as a fraction in its simplest form the part which is
   a patterned ▦ — a $\frac{1}{4}$
   b unshaded ☐ — b $\frac{3}{5}$
   c shaded. ▦ — c $\frac{3}{20}$

4. 3.75 × 8 = 30. Write the answers to
   a 375 × 8 — a 3000
   b 3.75 × 80. — b 300
5. A holiday started on 25 August and ended on 7 September. For how many days did the holiday last? — 14
6. What fraction in its simplest form is equivalent to
   a 0.6 — a $\frac{3}{5}$
   b 0.16? — b $\frac{4}{25}$
7. The mean mass of three parcels is 6kg. Two of the parcels have a mass of 4.6kg and 6kg. Find the mass of the third parcel. — 7.4kg
8. A sheet of plywood 26cm by 8cm is cut into strips 2cm wide. (8cm, 26cm) Find the total length of the strips. — 104cm
9. 1ml or 1cm³ of water has a mass of 1g. Find the mass of water in kilograms
   a in a can which holds $1\frac{3}{4}$l — a 1.75kg
   b in a tank the volume of which is 6400cm³. — b 6.4kg
10. Seven buns cost £2.47. Find to the nearest penny the cost of one. — 35p
11. The circumference of the wheel is 1.5m. How many metres will the wheel travel in
    a 10 turns — a 15m
    b 100 turns? — b 150m
12. The price of $\frac{1}{2}$kg of potatoes was increased from 30p to 36p. Find the increase as a fraction in its simplest form of the original price. — $\frac{1}{5}$

A

		Answer
1	$5.305 = 5 + \frac{\blacksquare}{1000}$	$\frac{305}{1000}$
2	10% of sixteen thousand =	1600
3	4.375kg = $\blacksquare$ g	4375g
4	£2 − (27p + 65p) = £$\blacksquare$	£1.08
5	2l 450ml − 0.5l = $\blacksquare$ ml	1950ml
6	0.4 + $\blacksquare$ = 0.476	0.076
7	£1.76 × 5 =	£8.80
8	0.75km = $\blacksquare$ m + 325m	425m
9	$\frac{x}{100} = 13.07$ Find x.	$\frac{1307}{100}$
10	38min + 2h + 47min = $\blacksquare$ h $\blacksquare$ min	3h 25min
11	a 10% of £20.40 =	a £2.04
	b $2\frac{1}{2}$% of £20.40 =	b £0.51
12	$\frac{1}{6}$ of 45cm = $\blacksquare$ mm	75mm

B

		Answer
1	Which of these numbers are factors of 75? 5 6 3 7 9	3 5
2	Find the mean of 3, 1.4, 2 and 2.6.	2.25
3	Write a $\frac{47}{8}$ as a mixed number	a $5\frac{7}{8}$
	b $5\frac{5}{6}$ as an improper fraction.	b $\frac{35}{6}$
4	What is the cost of 400g at £1.50 per $\frac{1}{2}$kg?	£1.20
5	By how many is 450 × 1000 less than $\frac{1}{2}$ million?	50000
6	By how many degrees does the temperature fall from 8°C to −5°C?	13°C
7	25% of Max's money is £35. Find the whole amount.	£140
8	Approximate to the nearest whole number.	
	a 79.63	a 80
	b 12.475	b 12
9	By how many millimetres is 95.4cm less than 1m?	46mm
10	Find the least number of pennies which must be added to 92p to make the amount exactly divisible by 6.	4
11	What percentage of 2l is	
	a 400ml	a 20%
	b 100ml?	b 5%

12 Find the volume of the box in cm³. 5cm 8cm 6cm

240cm³

C

		Answer
1	By how many thousandths is 1.057 less than 2?	943 thousandth
2	A —— O (130°) B By how many degrees is the reflex angle at O greater than the obtuse angle at O?	100°
3	Ellie spends $\frac{1}{2}$ of her money on bus fares and $\frac{5}{12}$ on sweets. What fraction of her money is left?	$\frac{1}{12}$
4	A cyclist travelled at 24 km/h for $\frac{1}{4}$ hour. How far did she travel?	6km
5	5kg 6kg Read as accurately as possible the mass shown by the pointer. Write the answer in grams.	5650g
6	The population of Town A is a quarter of a million. The population of Town B is fifty thousand less than Town A. What is the population of Town B?	200000
7	How much change is there out of £15 after spending £9.50 and £3.20?	£2.30
8	Write these decimals in ascending order. 5.03 0.35 0.5 3.05 3.5	0.35 0.5 3.05 3.5 5.03
9	A bus runs at intervals of 25 min. What are the times of the next two buses after 08:15?	08:40 09:05
10	Buy today for £60 or pay 10% weekly for 12 weeks. By how much is it cheaper to pay today?	£12
11	A rectangular path is 9m long and 80cm wide. Find its area in m².	7.2m²
12	Ravi is given £85 as birthday gifts. He spends 30% and saves the remainder.	
	a What percentage does he save?	a 70%
	b How much money does he spend?	b £25.50

A | Answer

1. Write in digits six hundred and two thousand five hundred and eight. — 602 508

2. £0.27 × 40 = — £10.80

3. $\frac{2}{3}$ of 960 = — 640

4. a 1% of £17 = ☐p — a 17p

   b 7% of £17 = £☐ — b £1.19

5. 10.06 = ☐ thousandths — 10 060 thousandths

6. £2.30 = three 50ps + two 20ps + ☐ 10ps — 4 10ps

7. $3\frac{3}{4}$ × 4 = — 15

8. 180° – (72° + 36°) = — 72°

9. 300g + 450g + 350g = ☐ kg — 1.1kg

10. 2h 15min – 50min = ☐h ☐min — 1h 25min

11. 27cm × 7 = ☐m ☐cm — 1m 89cm

12. $\frac{£16.56}{8}$ = — £2.07

B | Answer

1. By how many is 0.3 million less than $\frac{1}{2}$ million? — 200 000

2. What length in metres is 6 times 7m 30cm? — 43.8m

3. How many times is $2\frac{1}{2}$ contained in 50? — 20

4. Find the total of 17p, 53p, 24p and 7p. Write the answer in £s. — £1.01

5. Write the 24-hour clock time which is 7h before 4.35 a.m. — 21:35

6. What fraction in its simplest form is equal to

   a 8% — a $\frac{2}{25}$

   b 35%? — b $\frac{7}{20}$

7. By what quantity is 920ml less than 1.2l? — 280ml

8. Increase £30.50 by 10%. — £33.55

9. If the distance from A to D is 14km, find the distance from B to C. — 7.05km

   A 4.7km B   C 2.25km D

10. Find the cost of 0.3m at £4.80 per metre. — £1.44

11. The perimeter of a rectangle is 65cm. Its length is 24cm. Find its width. — 8.5cm

12. 10 doughnuts cost £2.09. Find the cost of one to the nearest penny. — 21p

C | Answer

1. How many envelopes costing 3p each can be bought for £2.40? — 80

2. ABCD is a parallelogram. Find in degrees

   a ∠ BAD — a 140°

   b ∠ ABC. — b 40°

3. Share £5 between Henry and Amy so that Henry has 6p each time Amy has 4p. How much does each have?

   Henry — £3

   Amy — £2

4. A man walked steadily at 4km/h from 11.00 a.m. to 2.30 p.m. How far did he walk? — 14km

5. From the largest of these decimal fractions take the smallest.

   | 0.33 0.3 0.03 0.333 | — 0.303

6. 1cm³ or 1ml of water has a mass of 1g. A jar holds $3\frac{1}{2}$l of water. Find

   a the volume of water in cm³ — a 3500cm³

   b the mass of the water in kg. — b 3.5kg

7. How much is saved by buying 15kg at 16p per kilogram, instead of the same mass at 9p per $\frac{1}{2}$kg? — 30p

8.

	Date of birth
Riaz	1.3.96
Sophie	1.10.94

   Find the age on 1 September 2010 in years and months of

   a Riaz — a 14yr 6mth

   b Sophie. — b 15yr 11mth

9. The area of a hall is 60m². Its length is 8m. Find

   a its width — a 7.5m

   b its perimeter. — b 31m

10. a What fraction of the circumference of the circle is the arc AB? — a $\frac{1}{3}$

    b If the circumference measures 188.4cm, find in millimetres the length of the arc. — b 628mm

11. Cheese costs £2.60 per $\frac{1}{2}$kg. Find the mass in kilograms and grams of cheese which costs £7.80. — 1kg 500g

12. Box A measures 8cm long, 9cm wide, 4cm high. Box B measures 10cm long, $5\frac{1}{2}$cm wide, 6cm high. Find the difference in their volumes. — 42cm³

A | Answer

1. $10 \times 10 \times 10 \times 10 \times 10 =$ — 100 000
2. $67p \times 6 = £$ ▨ — £4.02
3. $(49 + 8) = 100 -$ ▨ — 43
4. 90% of £300 = — £270
5. $5l \div 8 =$ ▨ ml — 625ml
6. $10 - 7\frac{3}{10} =$ — $2\frac{7}{10}$
7. $0.246 = 2$ tenths + ▨ thousandths — 46 thousandths
8. a $\frac{3}{25} =$ ▨ % — a 12%
   b $0.07 =$ ▨ % — b 7%
9. $1.25kg - 600g =$ ▨ g — 650g
10. nine 5ps + three 2ps + three 20ps = £ ▨ — £1.11
11. $\frac{3}{4}$ of 3.6cm = ▨ mm — 27mm
12. 2h 49min + 53min = ▨ h ▨ min — 3h 42min

B | Answer

1. By how many is 90 200 less than one hundred thousand? — 9800
2. Find the total number of days in February, March and April in a leap year. — 90 days
3.

    How many degrees in the reflex angle AOB? — 288°

   (diagram: circle with centre O, angle 72° between A and B)
4. Find the cost of 90cm of cloth at £3.70 per metre. — £3.33
5. How many times is 400g contained in 2.4kg? — 6
6. Of these numbers which is the smallest?

    | 1.11 | 1.01 | 1.111 | 1.1 |

    — 1.01
7. What is the difference in millilitres between 2.8l and 3.7l? — 900ml
8. Write as a fraction in its lowest terms.
   a £4.50 of £18 — a $\frac{1}{4}$
   b 5min of 1h — b $\frac{1}{12}$
9. A strip of plastic 4m 200mm long is cut into seven equal pieces. Find in millimetres the length of each piece. — 600mm
10. Approximate
    a £29.50 to the nearest £ — a £30
    b $\frac{99}{2}$p to the nearest 1p. — b 50p
11. $5\overline{)\,9\ 3\ p}$ $£x$ Find the sum of money which was divided by 5. — £4.65
12. The diameters of two circles are 9.4cm and 15.8cm. What is the radius of each circle in millimetres? — 47mm 79mm

C | Answer

1. Which numbers below 50 have both 2 and 7 as factors? — 14 28 42
2. What is the date of the third Wednesday in July if 1 July is a Sunday? — 18 July
3.

June	July	Aug	Sept
40mm	23mm	42mm	35mm

    The monthly rainfall is given in millimetres. Find the mean rainfall for all four months. — 35mm
4. 60kg of mortar is mixed from 4 parts of sand and 1 part of cement. Find the mass used of a sand — a 48kg
   b cement. — b 12kg
5. Write this number in words.
   $(7 \times 10^3) + (1 \times 10^2) + (9 \times 10)$
   seven thousand one hundred and ninety
6. How many degrees are there in a turn from W to SE
   a clockwise — a 225°
   b anticlockwise. — b 135°
7.

    The diameter of circle A is 9.4cm. The diameter of circle B is 5.8cm.

    How far apart are the two centre points in millimetres? — 76mm
8. a Find the area of a square with 5cm sides. — a 25cm²
   b How many times greater is the area of a square with sides double that length? — b 4
9.

    | Stickers |
    | 7p each or 6 for 40p |

    How much money is saved by buying 24 stickers in groups of six? — 8p
10.

    AB and CD are parallel lines. Find
    a angle x — a 135°
    b angle y. — b 45°

    (diagram: lines with 135° angle, x and y marked)
11. Grace won a prize of £800 which she deposited in a bank at an interest rate of 5%. How much interest did she receive at the end of 1 year? — £40
12.

    a How many cm cubes can be fitted into the bottom of the box? — a 60

    (diagram: box 6cm by 10cm)

    b If the volume of the box is 240cm³, find its height. — b 4cm

Mental Arithmetic 4 Answers

SECTION 3 | Test 12

A | Answer

1. $55 + 17 = \blacksquare \times 9$ — 8
2. £0.95 = 50p + 20p + $\blacksquare$ 5ps — 5 5ps
3. 2.3m – 90cm = $\blacksquare$ cm — 140cm
4. 1 000 000 = $\blacksquare$ thousands — 1000 Th
   = $\blacksquare$ hundreds — 10 000 H
5. 380g × 9 = $\blacksquare$ kg — 3.42kg
6. 7 × y = 7532. Find y. — 1076
7. a 10% of £27 = £$\blacksquare$ — a £2.70
   b 1% of £27 = $\blacksquare$ p — b 27p
8. $\frac{1}{2} + \frac{3}{8} + \frac{3}{4} =$ — $1\frac{5}{8}$
9. 2.05l + $\blacksquare$ ml = $2\frac{1}{2}$l — 450ml
10. 360° – (75° + 80° + 130°) = — 75°
11. $\frac{5}{6}$ of £90 = — £75
12. 4.07 × 8 = — 32.56

B | Answer

1. Which of the numbers are multiples of 4, 6 and 9?

   | 24 | 36 | 54 | 60 | 72 |

   — 36 72
2. How many kilometres are there in seventeen hundred metres? — 1.7km
3. Decrease €44 by 10%. — €39.60
4. How many hours and minutes from 09:48 to 11:19? — 1h 31min
5. What fraction in its simplified form is
   a the patterned part $\boxplus$ — a $\frac{2}{3}$
   b the shaded part $\blacksquare$ — b $\frac{1}{4}$
   c the unshaded part $\square$ — c $\frac{1}{12}$
6. Find the cost of 2.25l at 28p per litre. — 63p
7. How many biscuits each costing 7p are bought for £2.73? — 39
8. Write each score as a percentage.
   a 18 out of 20 — a 90%
   b 35 out of 35 — b 100%
9. Five oranges cost 80p. What fraction of 80p will three oranges cost? — $\frac{3}{5}$
10. By how many is 300 050 greater than $\frac{1}{4}$ million? — 50 050
11. Find $\frac{1}{5}$ of £1.68 to the nearest penny. — 34p
12. Find in cm³ the volume of a box 15cm by 10cm by 7cm. — 1050cm³

C | Answer

1. Find the missing numbers in this sequence.
   0.125, 0.25, 0.375, $\blacksquare$, $\blacksquare$ — 0.5 0.625
2. What number when added to 48 three times gives a total of 120? — 24
3. A fruit cake has a mass of 1.5kg. If 40% of the mass is fruit, find the mass of the fruit in grams. — 600g
4. A line 8cm long is drawn to the scale 1mm to 0.1m. What length does the line represent? — 8m
5. Which of these fractions is less than $\frac{1}{4}$?

   | $\frac{1}{3}$ | $\frac{3}{10}$ | $\frac{2}{5}$ | $\frac{1}{6}$ | $\frac{3}{8}$ |

   — $\frac{1}{6}$
6. A snow removal vehicle spreads grit at the rate of 125g per 1m². How many kilograms are required to grit a path 50m²? — 6.25kg
7. How far will a cyclist travel in $\frac{1}{4}$ hour if he cycles at 18 kilometres per hour? — $4\frac{1}{2}$ km
8. The length of a rectangle is three times its width. If the perimeter is 192cm find
   a the length — a 72cm
   b the width of the rectangle. — b 24cm
9. O is the centre of the circle the radius of which is 7.4cm. Find
   a the angle at the centre AOB — a 60°
   b the length of the straight line AB. — b 7.4cm
10. Of 150 children in a school 60 can swim one width of the pool and 45 can swim one length of the pool. What percentage of the children can swim
    a the width — a 40%
    b the length? — b 30%
11. Seven children shared a money prize equally. Each child received £42 and there was £6 left. Find the total value of the prize. — £300
12. The drawing shows a block of gold. Find its volume. — 300cm³

43

Schofield & Sim

A

5 + 6 = 11	10 × 10 = 100	(6 × 6) + 5 = 41	27 × 8 = 21_
8 + 8 = 16	4 × 7 = 28	(9 × 1) + 7 = 16	49 × 6 = 29_
0 + 7 = 7	9 × 3 = 27	(5 × 8) + 4 = 44	107 × 7 = 74_
7 + 8 = 15	8 × 6 = 48	(8 × 0) + 6 = 6	93 × 10 = 93_
4 + 7 = 11	1 × 8 = 8	(10 × 5) + 8 = 58	180 × 10 = 180_
18 + 9 = 27	5 × 9 = 45	(8 × 8) + 6 = 70	95 × 20 = 190_
15 + 8 = 23	7 × 7 = 49	(3 × 3) + 2 = 11	86 × 40 = 344_
3 + 29 = 32	0 × 0 = 0	(9 × 8) + 7 = 79	100 × 80 = 800_
7 + 36 = 43	4 × 8 = 32	(4 × 9) + 5 = 41	98 × 100 = 980_
14 + 19 = 33	9 × 7 = 63	(7 × 6) + 3 = 45	204 × 100 = 2040_
12 − 5 = 7	24 ÷ 3 = 8	29 ÷ 3 = 9 r 2	102 ÷ 3 = 3_
9 − 0 = 9	40 ÷ 8 = 5	67 ÷ 8 = 8 r 3	336 ÷ 4 = 8_
11 − 3 = 8	0 ÷ 6 = 0	21 ÷ 4 = 5 r 1	648 ÷ 6 = 10_
14 − 5 = 9	54 ÷ 9 = 6	6 ÷ 7 = 0 r 6	590 ÷ 10 = 5_
15 − 9 = 6	7 ÷ 7 = 1	39 ÷ 5 = 7 r 4	800 ÷ 10 = 8_
24 − 6 = 18	42 ÷ 7 = 6	70 ÷ 9 = 7 r 7	540 ÷ 20 = 2_
26 − 9 = 17	81 ÷ 9 = 9	51 ÷ 6 = 8 r 3	420 ÷ 60 = _
32 − 8 = 24	36 ÷ 4 = 9	13 ÷ 7 = 1 r 6	1050 ÷ 50 = 2_
58 − 9 = 49	63 ÷ 9 = 7	52 ÷ 5 = 10 r 2	4000 ÷ 100 = 4_
47 − 20 = 27	56 ÷ 8 = 7	4 ÷ 9 = 0 r 4	2900 ÷ 100 = 2_

B Write these numbers.

Fifty thousand and seven	50 007
Sixty-two thousand four hundred and two	62 402
One hundred and forty thousand and eleven	140 011
Two hundred and six thousand and nine	206 009
30 000 + 400 + 6 =	30 406
100 000 + 7000 + 50 + 8 =	107 058
(4 × 1000) + (6 × 100) + (3 × 10) + 8 =	4638
(9 × 1000) + (7 × 10) + 5 =	9075
(3 × 1000) + (4 × 10) =	3040
1 million	1 000 000
$1\frac{1}{2}$ million	1 500 000
$\frac{1}{4}$ million	250 000
2.7 million	2 700 000

C Write as decimals.

47 tenths	4.7
201 tenths	20.1
4 hundredths	0.04
309 hundredths	3.09
580 hundredths	5.8
603 thousandths	0.603
75 thousandths	0.075
3009 thousandths	3.009
$9 + \frac{3}{10} + \frac{8}{100} =$	9.38
$10 + \frac{7}{100} + \frac{2}{1000} =$	10.072
5 tenths + 2 hundredths =	0.52
17 hundredths and 6 thousandths =	0.176

How many tenths equal

6.8	6_
14.9	14_
30.4?	30_

How many hundredths equal

0.93	9_
7.05	70_
3.2?	32_

How many thousandths equal

0.003	_
0.078	78
1.52	152_
2.8	280_
4.09?	409_

D

5.03 + 0.7 = 5.73	6.45 × 10 = 64.5	79 ÷ 10 = 7.9	**E** Find the value of x.
2.5 + 1.54 = 4.04	0.873 × 10 = 8.73	40.2 ÷ 10 = 4.02	x + 7 = 24 1_
0.06 + 1.04 = 1.1	2.03 × 100 = 203	34 ÷ 100 = 0.34	5 + x = 32 2_
3.7 + 0.35 = 4.05	0.092 × 100 = 9.2	10.7 ÷ 100 = 0.107	x + 1.5 = 5 3._
0.28 + 1.625 = 1.905	1.64 × 1000 = 1640	608 ÷ 1000 = 0.608	31 − x = 16 15
	0.053 × 1000 = 53	1035 ÷ 1000 = 1.035	x − 6.3 = 10 16._
2 − 1.4 = 0.6	1.8 × 5 = 9	5.6 ÷ 8 = 0.7	10 × x = 25 2.5
1.4 − 0.9 = 0.5	4 × 1.63 = 6.52	10.25 ÷ 5 = 2.05	x × 4 = 18 4._
10 − 8.75 = 1.25	0.09 × 8 = 0.72	0.636 ÷ 6 = 0.106	7 = $\frac{x}{5}$ 3_
4.8 − 3.76 = 1.04	7 × 2.08 = 14.56	4.77 ÷ 9 = 0.53	$\frac{x}{10}$ = 0.6 _
0.7 − 0.58 = 0.12	1.063 × 6 = 6.378	8.032 ÷ 8 = 1.004	9 + x = 7 × 7 40

A Fill in the missing numerator or denominator.

$\frac{3}{4} = \frac{12}{16}$ $\frac{2}{3} = \frac{8}{12}$ $\frac{7}{8} = \frac{21}{24}$ $\frac{5}{6} = \frac{15}{18}$ $\frac{4}{5} = \frac{40}{50}$ $\frac{3}{10} = \frac{30}{100}$

Write each fraction in its simplest form.

$\frac{9}{12} = \frac{3}{4}$ $\frac{12}{18} = \frac{2}{3}$ $\frac{20}{25} = \frac{4}{5}$ $\frac{24}{30} = \frac{4}{5}$ $\frac{70}{100} = \frac{7}{10}$ $\frac{45}{100} = \frac{9}{20}$

Change each improper fraction to a mixed number.

$\frac{19}{4} = 4\frac{3}{4}$ $\frac{31}{5} = 6\frac{1}{5}$ $\frac{43}{8} = 5\frac{3}{8}$ $\frac{29}{6} = 4\frac{5}{6}$ $\frac{77}{10} = 7\frac{7}{10}$ $\frac{40}{3} = 13\frac{1}{3}$

Change each mixed number to an improper fraction.

$7\frac{3}{4} = \frac{31}{4}$ $8\frac{2}{3} = \frac{26}{3}$ $5\frac{4}{5} = \frac{29}{5}$ $9\frac{7}{10} = \frac{97}{10}$ $4\frac{7}{8} = \frac{39}{8}$ $10\frac{5}{6} = \frac{65}{6}$

B Write as a fraction in its simplest form.

50 of 75	$\frac{2}{3}$
30p of £1.00	$\frac{3}{10}$
25cm of 1m	$\frac{1}{4}$
12kg of 30kg	$\frac{2}{5}$
70 of 100	$\frac{7}{10}$
800g of 1kg	$\frac{4}{5}$
400ml of 2l	$\frac{1}{5}$
45 of 100	$\frac{9}{20}$

C Find

$\frac{3}{5}$ of 70	42
$\frac{5}{8}$ of 64	40
$\frac{7}{10}$ of £1.20	84p
$\frac{5}{6}$ of 42l	35l
$\frac{4}{7}$ of 350g	200g
$\frac{13}{100}$ of £1.00	13p
$\frac{2}{3}$ of 1200	800
$\frac{35}{100}$ of 1kg.	350g

Find the whole when

$\frac{1}{6}$ is 35	210
$\frac{3}{4}$ is 27p	36p
$\frac{4}{5}$ is 36cm	45cm
$\frac{7}{10}$ is £1.40	£2.00
$\frac{2}{3}$ is 800g	1200g
$\frac{5}{9}$ is 5000	9000
$\frac{3}{8}$ is 24l	64l
$\frac{9}{20}$ is £1.80	£4.00

D Write as percentages.

a 33 out of 100 **33%**   b 87 out of 100 **87%**   c 9 out of 100 **9%**   d 45 out of 100 **45%**

a 0.65 **65%**   b 0.38 **38%**   c 0.75 **75%**   d 0.3 **30%**

a $\frac{29}{100}$ **29%**   b $\frac{56}{100}$ **56%**   c $\frac{1}{100}$ **1%**   d $\frac{13}{100}$ **13%**

Change each fraction first to hundredths, then write it as a percentage.

a $\frac{19}{50} = \frac{38}{100} = $ **38%**   b $\frac{3}{25} = \frac{12}{100} = $ **12%**   c $\frac{13}{20} = \frac{65}{100} = $ **65%**

a $\frac{3}{4} = \frac{75}{100} = $ **75%**   b $\frac{4}{5} = \frac{80}{100} = $ **80%**   c $\frac{7}{10} = \frac{70}{100} = $ **70%**

Fill the blank spaces in each of the columns. The first is done for you.

	a	b	c	d	e	f	g	h	i	j	k	l	m
Fraction in its simplest form	$\frac{1}{2}$	$\frac{1}{4}$	$\frac{3}{4}$	$\frac{1}{5}$	$\frac{2}{5}$	$\frac{3}{5}$	$\frac{4}{5}$	$\frac{1}{10}$	$\frac{3}{10}$	$\frac{7}{10}$	$\frac{9}{10}$	$\frac{1}{20}$	$\frac{1}{100}$
Decimal fraction	0.5	0.25	0.75	0.2	0.4	0.6	0.8	0.1	0.3	0.7	0.9	0.05	0.01
Percentage	50%	25%	75%	20%	40%	60%	80%	10%	30%	70%	90%	5%	1%

E Find the value of

25% of 120	30
50% of 35	$17\frac{1}{2}$
75% of 400	300
10% of 1000	100
30% of 90	27
70% of 200	140
90% of 160	144
20% of 95p	19p
40% of £20	£8.00
60% of £15.	£9.00

Find the value of

50% of 14p	7p
20% of £6.50	£1.30
100% of 93p	93p
10% of 2.5kg	250g
5% of 4l	200ml
30% of 2m	60cm
1% of £1.00	1p
7% of £1.00	7p
3% of £3.00	9p
12% of £9.00.	£1.08

F Find as a percentage

6 of 24	25%
$7\frac{1}{2}$ of 15	50%
40p of 50p	80%
93p of 93p	100%
200g of $\frac{1}{2}$kg	40%
700ml of 1l	70%
25p of £2.50	10%
£1.50 of £2.00	75%
7p of £1.00	7%
30cm of 1.5m.	20%

Schofield & Sim

A

70p =	£0.70
2p =	£0.02
£0.63 =	63p
£0.19 =	19p
£0.04 =	4p
£1.37 =	13 10ps 7p
£3.09 =	15 20ps 9p
£10.80 =	108 10ps 0p
seven 10ps + six 2ps =	82p
three 50ps + nine 10ps =	£2.40
three 10ps + five 5ps + 9p =	64p
£0.85 = five 10ps + ▓ 5ps =	7 5ps
£1.20 = twelve 5ps + ▓ 20ps =	3 20ps
£2.30 = three 50ps + ▓ 20ps =	4 20ps

B

9p + 3p + 17p =	29p
15p + 8p + 6p =	29p
14p + 7p + 12p =	33p
5p + 11p + 15p + 4p =	35p
6p + 19p + 21p + 18p =	64p
37p + 85p =	£1.22
£1.03 + 49p =	£1.52
£2.57 + £0.60 =	£3.17
43p − 19p =	24p
95p − 18p =	77p
£1.10 − 84p =	26p
£1.70 − 93p =	77p
£2.30 − £0.80 =	£1.50
£2.06 − £1.40 =	66p

C Find the cost of

10 at 15p each	£1.50
100 at 3p each	£3.00
9 at 13p each	£1.17
8 at 27p each	£2.16
5 at 45p each	£2.25
19 at 4p each	76▓
27 at 7p each.	£1.89

Find the cost of 1 when

10 cost £2.70	27▓
100 cost £15	15▓
6 cost 84p	14▓
4 cost £0.72	18▓
7 cost £2.24	32▓
9 cost £3.06.	34▓

D Find the change from

20p after spending   a 3p   17p   b 8p   12p

20p after spending   a 12p   8p   b 14p   6p

50p after spending   a 37p   13p   b 19p   31p

c 26p   24p   d 5p   45p

£1 after spending   a 81p   19p   b 66p   34p

c 45p   55p   d 7p   93p

£5 after spending   a 73p £4.27   b £4.09   91p

c £2.54 £2.46   d £1.98 £3.02

E Make up the given amounts using the least number of coins. The first one is done for you.

Amount	50p	20p	10p	5p	2p	1p
23p		1			1	1
39p		1	1	1	2	
67p	1		1	1	1	
78p	1	1		1	1	1
86p	1	1	1	1		1
94p	1	2			2	

F

84cm =	0.84m
309cm =	3.09m
1075mm =	1.075m
2305mm =	2.305m
750mm =	0.75m
100m =	0.1km
925m =	0.925km
1605m =	1.605km
860g =	0.860kg
1400g =	1.4kg
700ml =	0.7l
3310ml =	3.31l

G

20.4cm =	204mm
1.5m =	1500mm
2.65m =	2650mm
0.85m =	85cm
8.37km =	8370m
0.6km =	600m
10.075km =	10075m
1.325kg =	1325g
0.05kg =	50g
3.72kg =	3720g
1.3l =	1300ml
4.25l =	4250ml

H Find the cost of

500g at 76p per kg	38▓
100g at 50p per kg	5▓
250g at 36p per kg	9▓
200g at £1.20 per kg	24▓
1.5kg at 64p per kg	96▓
100g at 45p per $\frac{1}{2}$kg	9▓
300g at £1.10 per $\frac{1}{2}$kg	66▓
25cm at 92p per m	23▓
10cm at £3.50 per m	35▓
60cm at £2.20 per m	£1.32
1.3l at 60p per l	78▓
800ml at 50p per l	40▓

I How many

min in $\frac{3}{4}$h	45min
min in $1\frac{1}{4}$h	75min
seconds in 5min	300s
weeks in 1 year	52wk
days in 1 year	365d
days in April	30d
days in July	31d
days in October?	31d

J Change to 24-hour clock times.

7.35 a.m.	07:35
12.05 p.m.	12:05
3.27 p.m.	15:27
10.55 p.m.	22:55

Change to 12-hour clock times. Use a.m. or p.m.

09:20	9.20 a.m.
14:56	2.56 p.m.
00:35	12.35 a.m.
21:16	9.16 p.m.

K Find the period of time between

8.35 a.m. and 10.16 a.m.	1h 41min
5.25 a.m. and noon	6h 35min
4.30 p.m. and 7.20 p.m.	2h 50min
11:35 and 14:15	2h 40min
03:40 and 06:10.	2h 30min

How many days inclusive

from 28 Jan to 9 Feb	13 d
from 17 May to 5 June	20 d
from 26 Nov to 3 Jan?	39 d

CHECK-UP TEST | Measurement and geometry

A Approximate to the nearest

whole number	49.55	50
whole number	$20\frac{2}{5}$	20
hundred	6057	6100
hundred	19 503	19 500
thousand	59 770	60 000
thousand	109 495	109 000
£1.00	£27.50	£28

B Approximate to the nearest

metre	8m 59cm	9m
metre	19m 700mm	20m
kilogram	16kg 50g	16kg
kilogram	7.55kg	8kg
$\frac{1}{2}$kg	9kg 800g	10kg
$\frac{1}{2}$kg	6.55kg	6.5kg
litre	39.87l	40l

Find to the nearest penny.   a $\frac{1}{10}$ of 97p __10p__   b $\frac{1}{3}$ of £2.50 __83p__   c $\frac{£3.35}{4}$ __84p__

C How many degrees in each of the angles x and y?

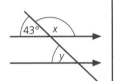

angle x __283°__   angle x __135°__   angle x __137°__

angle y __45°__   angle y __43°__

D Find the missing angle in each of the triangles. Then name each triangle according to
a the angles **b** the sides.

Angles in triangle			a Name of triangle (angles)	b Name of triangle (sides)
32°	58°	90°	right-angled	scalene
46°	52°	82°	acute-angled	scalene
60°	60°	60°	acute-angled	equilateral
17°	125°	38°	obtuse-angled	scalene
57°	57°	66°	acute-angled	isosceles

E

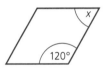

Find the angle x in   **a** the rhombus __60°__   **b** the trapezium __125°__

c the parallelogram __50°__   **d** the irregular quadrilateral __132°__

F Give the unit of measurement in the answer for each example.

perimeter of square __36cm__

area of square __81cm²__

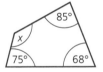

perimeter of rectangle __20.6cm__

area of rectangle __16.6cm²__

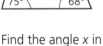

area of triangle __64cm²__

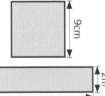

diameter of circle __10cm__

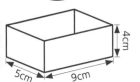

How many cm cubes

a fit into the bottom of the box   a __45__

b fill the box?   b __180__

Write the missing measurement in each of the rectangles.

Area	50m²	121.5cm²	25cm²	16m²
Length	5m	13.5cm	10cm	32m
Breadth	10m	9cm	2.5cm	50cm

Write the missing measurement in each of the triangles.

Base	16cm	45m	10cm	12cm
Height	8cm	12m	18cm	7cm
Area	64cm²	270m²	90cm²	42cm²

Write the missing radius or diameter.

Radius	15.3cm	18mm	4.9cm	27.6cm
Diameter	30.6cm	36mm	9.8cm	55.2cm

Find the volume of each of these boxes.

length 13cm, breadth 8cm, height 2cm __208cm³__

length 7cm, breadth 4cm, height 2.5cm __70cm³__

cube of 6cm side __216cm³__

Full list of Schofield & Sims Mental Arithmetic books

Pupil books

Mental Arithmetic Introductory Book	ISBN 978 07217 0798 3
Mental Arithmetic 1	ISBN 978 07217 0799 0
Mental Arithmetic 2	ISBN 978 07217 0800 3
Mental Arithmetic 3	ISBN 978 07217 0801 0
Mental Arithmetic 4	ISBN 978 07217 0802 7
Mental Arithmetic 5	ISBN 978 07217 0803 4
Mental Arithmetic 6	ISBN 978 07217 0804 1

Answer books

Mental Arithmetic Introductory Book Answers	ISBN 978 07217 0853 9
Mental Arithmetic 1 Answers	ISBN 978 07217 0805 8
Mental Arithmetic 2 Answers	ISBN 978 07217 0806 5
Mental Arithmetic 3 Answers	ISBN 978 07217 0807 2
Mental Arithmetic 4 Answers	ISBN 978 07217 0808 9
Mental Arithmetic 5 Answers	ISBN 978 07217 0809 6
Mental Arithmetic 6 Answers	ISBN 978 07217 0810 2

Teacher's Guide

Mental Arithmetic Teacher's Guide	ISBN 978 07217 1389 2

Free downloads

A range of free downloads is available from the Schofield & Sims website (www.schofieldandsims.co.uk). These downloads may be used to support pupils in their learning, both in school and at home. They include the following items:

- two **Mental Arithmetic** Entry Tests to help you choose the best book for each individual

- an Achievement Award certificate for each **Mental Arithmetic** book

- Maths Facts downloads to provide a quick reference tool

- a National Curriculum Chart to show how each book supports the programmes of study.